Twentieth Century Library

Albert Einstein

LEOPOLD INFELD

Albert Einstein

HIS WORK AND ITS INFLUENCE ON OUR WORLD

CHARLES SCRIBNER'S SONS, NEW YORK

CHARLES SCRIBNER'S SONS, LTD., LONDON

1950

Printed in the United States of America

A

The quotation which appears on page 5 is reprinted from *Relativity: The Special and General Theory* by Albert Einstein, 1920, Henry Holt & Company, Inc.; used by permission of Peter Smith, Publisher.

Quotations which appear on pages 116, 117, 118 and 119 are from *The World As I See It* by Albert Einstein. Copyright 1934 by Covici Friede. Reprinted by permission of Crown Publishers.

CONTENTS

Albert Einstein

CHAPTER ONE

OVERCOMING PREJUDICES

IN 1955 relativity theory will be half a century old. Today it is looked upon by physicists as a classical theory, and the turbulent times when it was disputed and attacked seem distant and forever past. Yet even as late as 1921 a distinguished physicist, von Laue, wrote in a preface to his scholarly book:

> Much admired and much cursed stands general relativity today. Those who shout loudest on both sides have one thing in common: they have a hearty ignorance of what they speak about.

Today, however, the shouts have subsided, relativity theory has become respectable and has taken its place as a cornerstone in the structure of modern physics. Its creator is looked upon as "the greatest living scientist" and his fame is more widespread than that of kings and presidents. It is time to look back, to view the Einstein revolutions as they developed and to see what their impact has been upon our age.

Let us first try to remove the effects of prejudices, meaningless slogans repeated thousands of times by word of mouth, by radio and by the press.

One of them claims that it is impossible for the ordinary person to understand Dr. Einstein's ideas. He is the high priest of mathematical learning and there are only twelve men who really understand him.

It is not easy to fight prejudices. I cannot even say that the statement about only twelve men understanding relativity theory is false. It is as meaningless as the statement "Only twelve men really understand Beethoven." Indeed, the analogy between mathematics and music, between Einstein and Beethoven, makes sense to anyone who loves mathematics and music.

Like music, mathematics and mathematical physics are artistic creations. As in music, we should distinguish between *technique* and *ideas*. No one can play Beethoven well, nor can anyone write a scientific paper on relativity theory, without first mastering the technique. Yet as one can experience deep emotion when listening to Beethoven while in complete ignorance of the technique of playing, so one can experience deep pleasure when grasping the basic ideas of relativity theory even if one is ignorant of the mathematical technique.

Actually there is no *one* understanding in science; it has different levels. We may, perhaps, succeed in choosing a level so high that only a few people could rise to it. But what few people? One of my colleagues (and a distinguished mathematician) has seriously voiced doubts whether Einstein is one of the three men who understand Einstein best.

Usually one assumes that a person either knows or does not know mathematics. The truth of the matter is that there are different levels of mathematical technique and they determine the level of deduction that can be reached by different men studying relativity theory.

One generally distinguishes, too, between *special* and *general* relativity theory. To know general relativity theory requires a higher knowledge of mathematics than to know special relativity theory. Yet the technique can be learned, and as time goes on the number of those initiated into the intricacies of mathematical relativity will increase.

On the scientific level there are hundreds who have written papers on relativity theory or subjects closely related to it. Like any other region of science, it is an open book. Though the number of new contributions is much smaller than in *quantum* theory, nevertheless it is still considerable. On the level of education, every good university turns out each year new students who understand the principles and the essential mathematical tools of relativity theory. When I was a student, relativity theory was not a part of the undergraduate curriculum. Nowadays, at least at some universities students in the third year learn the basic equations of special relativity theory and in the fourth year the mathematical theory of relativity. This year twenty-five students will graduate from my university with a fairly good knowledge of the principles of special and general relativity theory and its mathematical techniques.

The point that I am trying to make here seems to me important. Einstein could not be one of those few who have influenced our century most strongly if his ideas in physics were understood by only a few persons. Sometime in the future the principles of relativity theory may even be taught in high school. The underlying ideas are both simple and essential, although the process of translating results into ordinary language requires time. The number of people who have assimilated some of the ideas of relativity theory increases, and will continue to increase for a long time to come. This is the reason why Einstein has influenced our modern culture. Relativity theory is not only for high priests of learning. Later we shall see how this abstract web of thought has influenced our whole life. True, there were times, around 1917, when only a few people fully understood relativity theory. Around that time a physicist remarked to Professor Eddington, "You are one of three men who understand relativity theory." When a pained expression appeared on Eddington's face, the physicist said, "Professor Eddington, you shouldn't be embarrassed; you are too modest." Sir Arthur replied, "No, I am not embarrassed; I am only wondering who is the third."

As all the sciences, so relativity theory is based on assumptions that are consistent with experiment. From these assumptions we deduce, and mathematics is the tool by which deductions are made. If the more advanced developments of this tool are unknown to the reader, as we shall assume, then we must omit most of the deductions. Yet we may still grasp some of the basic ideas and some of the results, even if we have to leave out the chain of reasoning that leads from the basic assumptions to the final conclusions that can be tested by experiment. We shall have to translate some of the assumptions and results, through analogies and pictures, from the abstract language of mathematics into our everyday language.

To do all this means to "popularize." And when we come to the problem of popularizing relativity theory, then we meet another deeply rooted prejudice worth discussing.

Many believe that relativity theory tells us that ours is a kind of Alice-in-Wonderland universe; that this was revealed by the mathematician Einstein who discovered that there is a fourth dimension, that objects shorten or elongate, that our world shrinks or expands like a balloon; that, in short, everything is relative and mysterious. That it is not your train that stops at Princeton, but it is Princeton that stops at your train. And out of this fantastic, relative world that Einstein created there suddenly appeared the atomic bomb.

Scientific methods of reasoning seem so different from those used in our ordinary life, because they are more refined, more elaborate and sophisticated. Yet, essentially, they are the same. If we don't cross the street because a car approaches, we are using theories, we are reasoning and deducing. The chain of deduction is in this case so short that it may almost be called instinct. In science, the chain is incomparably longer. It is much longer in relativity theory than in classical mechanics. As science progresses, this chain becomes longer and longer and, therefore, harder and harder to grasp. But the tree of science grows from the soil of our experiences. This is true of relativity theory too.

How, then, did the prejudice about the mysterious relative Alice-in-Wonderland universe arise?

In 1916, when relativity theory was known mainly among German physicists and mathematicians, but hardly known to the public at large, Einstein wrote a small, non-technical book about special and general relativity theory. Here are some excerpts from his preface; almost precisely the kind of things that I would like to write as an introduction to this book:

> . . . the book is written for those . . . who are interested in the general philosophical . . . point of view and do not have the knowledge of the mathematical formalism . . . ; it assumes much patience and will power on the part of the reader. The author took great pains to put forward the ideas clearly and simply . . . In the interest of clarity, I did not hesitate to repeat myself and did not pay the slightest attention to the elegance of presentation; I sincerely stuck to the prescription of the great theoretician L. Boltzmann, that the business of elegance should be left to the tailors and shoemakers. (*Relativity: The Special and General Theory*)

Einstein's small book became a classic. Later, around 1920, when the fame of relativity and its creator spread all over the world, hundreds of books, pamphlets, articles in journals and newspapers were printed about Einstein and relativity, starting an era of hucksterism in popular science.

Soon it was found that books which startle the reader, mixing science with mystery and drama, have a greater appeal than those, like Einstein's, that present the basic ideas in a straightforward, almost colorless, manner. Thus, the examples introduced by Einstein were worked over endlessly by others, and at the same time they were embroidered with unnecessary frills; everything possible was done to make the scenery more striking and on it to paint the scientist as a devilishly clever fellow who snatches the mysteries that nature cagily tries to hide from his eyes. These books evoked metaphysical thrills; it was possible to read them with excitement and a feeling of drama, while understanding nothing. Some of the popularizing authors wrote with great artistic skill and a new style of popularization (which is, I believe, now dying out) was developed, and this is what engendered the prejudice about the mysteries of the universe and science.

Science is a rational structure; the greatest pleasure in studying is that of understanding. Without it knowledge means little. The existence of science and its progress is based upon the belief that the universe is not capricious or mysterious. As a great mathematician Poincaré said (he, by the way, was himself very near to the discovery of special relativity theory), the greatest miracle is that miracles do not happen.

The object of our reasoning in life and in science is the same: to order and predict events; to understand the world of our sense impressions. The difficulties inherent in relativity theory are inherent everywhere in modern physics. In it we do not deal with things as familiar and tangible as the boiling temperature of water, or the motion of a pendulum, or the amount of pressure in a cylinder. But even these simple phenomena were as abstract and difficult to grasp for the ordinary citizen about the time they were discovered as the red-shift of the spectral lines or the deflection of light rays is today.

The phenomena that modern physics explains are essentially those produced in modern laboratories with their cyclotrons, mass spectrographs, and Geiger counters; or astronomical phenomena like the curving of the light rays from the stars when they pass the edge of the sun during an eclipse; or the phenomena of new particles created by cosmic rays. Even the phenomena that happen in the laboratory of the universe are caught, measured and analyzed by the most sensitive instruments devised by man. Every scientific theory, though speculative in its character, is meaningful only if it can be tested by experiment. It dies if it fails such tests.

Thus we shall approach Einstein's theory as the rational structure that it is: in part philosophical and speculative, yet capable of experimental verification. It is neither metaphysical nor mysterious.

Ten years ago relativity theory seemed an abstract web of thought, far removed from the phenomena that men can witness or experience. Not so today. Not so since 80,000 died in Hiroshima. The relativistic relation between mass and energy, found by Einstein in 1905, is no longer a rare laboratory phenomenon. To all of us it has become a matter of life and death.

Relativity was not born solely because of Einstein's genius, but it was he who accomplished the revolution for which science had become ripe. Chosen to lead the revolution, he was the most peaceful of men, an outsider, not even a member of the academic profession. He was, in 1905, a young Ph.D., twenty-six years old, just married and a clerk in the patent office in Berne, Switzerland. He was shy, kind and friendly. He studied little but thought much; he had a great capacity for wonder and accepted no man's dogma. I do not believe that he ever had the makings of a good clerk, but Switzerland did not expell him from the civil service. He was allowed to think and dream and write papers that changed the face of science.

CHAPTER TWO

BEFORE THE EINSTEIN REVOLUTION

THE ORIGIN OF THE ETHER CONCEPT

REVOLUTIONS in science, like all great historical upheavals, break out when times are ripe for them. To understand what they are and why they come it is necessary to analyze the times in which they occur.

The first Einstein revolution came about much sooner because Einstein lived. Yet in the physics at the end of the late nineteenth century we find the seeds from which Einstein's great work of clarification grew. To understand his achievement we must examine the state of physics at the turn of our century. We shall look at it from the heights reached by modern science, and the picture must necessarily be vague, for we shall attempt to view a vast land in which details will be blurred. Against this general background we shall analyze a few isolated points which later became the foci of the revolution. They seemed much less important before relativity theory was formulated, for it was only relativity theory that illuminated these points and led to an understanding of the grave difficulties inherent in classical physics.

We start, therefore, with a very general picture of nineteenth-century physics. To be concrete, we shall have to think of it in terms of two main branches. We shall call them briefly the *mechanical* and the *field* theories.

Each of these branches we shall connect with one man's

name. This is so great a simplification as almost to falsify the entire picture, for if we call the mechanical branch, alternatively, *Newtonian* physics, we only continue the illusion that a doctrine can spring forth in complete form from a single man's head. In point of fact, the foundations of Newtonian theory lie in the work of Galileo and although, if we go deeper into the past, the links of the historical chain become weaker, nevertheless, connections with the past still exist. But once we are aware of this important historical continuity in science, there is little impropriety in connecting mechanistic physics with the name of Newton, whose celebrated work *Philosophiae Naturalis Principia Mathematica* (1687) constituted an epoch-making formulation of the mechanical world-view.

Similarly, we shall connect the field theory with the name of Maxwell, though Maxwell's ideas, too, were based on the work of Faraday and later confirmed experimentally by Hertz. James Clerk Maxwell died in 1879, the year in which Albert Einstein was born.

The different elements of the mechanical and field views can be traced as far back as the ancient philosophies. Yet it was only the science of the nineteenth century that developed these two views fully in all their mathematical beauty. The two branches of physics existing side by side represent the end product of a long and dynamic growth.

It is not difficult to distinguish between the mechanical and the field views. Nowadays both these aspects of science have penetrated even into our ordinary language, and, while talking about the world around us, we describe fragments of it as though they were interpreted in terms of either the mechanical or the field theory.

Thus, if we say that because of gravitational attraction the earth moves around the sun along a path called an ellipse, we are employing the Newtonian view, the mechanical language. Such a statement might have sounded sophisticated in Newton's times, but it is commonplace today. To be explicit: we draw a point—the sun, at the focus of an ellipse—and another point, the earth, on its periphery. The two bodies—earth and sun—are represented by these two points or particles, mutually attracted by gravitational force. These are the characteristic features of the mechanical or Newtonian view: *particles and simple forces acting between them*. It was just this view that became most successful in the region of mechanics and astronomy, later invading other branches of physics.

It is not surprising that the nineteenth century tried to apply a mechanical interpretation to all realms of natural phenomena. In Newton's time, mechanics was the oldest, most familiar and most successful member of the scientific family. Thus, to explain the phenomena of heat, light and flowing fluids meant to invent an appropriate mechanical picture. This is what is meant by the assertion that the mechanical view reigned over physics. Up to the nineteenth century, no one imagined that this mechanical regime could be overthrown. The development of science seemed then to be mapped out along mechanistic lines for the entire future of our civilization. The celebrated mathematician Lagrange, who died in the early nineteenth century, remarked that Newton was not only the greatest but the most fortunate among scientists, because the science of our world can be created only once, and it was Newton who created it. From our present vantage point it is clear that the foundations of science have been created and re-created and that Newton's great achievement was the creation of only the first link in a chain of scientific revolutions. Nevertheless, when Lagrange lived, and even later, almost throughout the first half of the nineteenth century, the mechanical view spread and deepened until it assumed the status of a philosophical dogma. Laplace, and later Helmholtz, formulated it with great imagination, reaching far beyond the known and explored region.

In those times, scientists assumed that our entire universe, and we in it, form a gigantic complicated machine that obeys Newtonian laws. If we know the present state of a mechanical system, that is, the positions and velocities of all particles, and if we also know the forces acting between these particles, then we can predict the future of such a system or disclose its past. Indeed, to solve a mechanical problem means to do just this.

Consequently, if the universe itself is one gigantic complicated machine and if we knew its state at a certain moment and the nature of all forces, we could predict the future of our universe to the smallest details and at an arbitrarily distant moment. Substituting different values of time in our resulting formulas, we could disclose its past as well. The scientist of the nineteenth century realized that he was far from such an ultimate goal. He was aware that he knew little about the state of our universe, and little about the laws that govern matter, much less those that govern life and thought. Yet there seemed to be nothing that prevented the wider and wider application of the mechanical view, so that the idea of all natural phenomena eventually being explained by Newtonian physics was looked upon as a theoretically attainable goal.

What about the other branch of physics—the *field* theory? The development of the field view in the second half of the nineteenth century introduced crucial ideas which ultimately brought about the decline of the mechanical view.

The field concept, too, has penetrated into our everyday language. Thus, if we say that electromagnetic waves spread from an antenna and affect radio receivers, we are using (at least to a certain degree) the field language. Such a sentence, commonplace today, would have been meaningless to the physicists of the early nineteenth century.

Maxwell's theory, which governs electrical and optical phenomena, is a *field* theory because in it the essential element is the description of *changes* that spread continuously through *space* in *time*. Thus, the concept of the field stands in contrast to the concept of simple particles in the mechanical view. (The differences between the two theories are also reflected mathematically: the equations of mechanics are ordinary differential equations, while the equations of the field are partial differential equations.)

An antenna sends electromagnetic waves, to which our radios react. The atoms in the sun or in a neon tube, or in an electric bulb, emit light to which our eye reacts. How unlike these two pictures are! In one of them we have an antenna and a radio receiver. In the other, the atom—itself a small antenna—sends out electromagnetic waves, and the detector—our eye—analyzes them, revealing the colors and shapes of the visible world. But these two different phenomena are both governed by the same laws: Maxwell's equations. Both the waves emitted from an antenna and an atom are electromagnetic waves that spread through space with the speed of 186,000 miles per second. Great progress in science can here be traced to the discovery of unexpected similarities and even identities beneath the surface of external differences.

The field view proved as successful in the domain of electrical and optical phenomena as the mechanical view had been in astronomy. From X rays to radio waves, including the visible waves of light, all this rich and wide world of radiation is governed by field laws which seem to have little in common with the mechanical view.

No orthodox physicist of the nineteenth century would have agreed with such an interpretation. The idea of two different physics, two alternative methods of thought, would have been unacceptable to him. He would have insisted that the field view is not essentially different from the mechanical view and that a consistent and completely satisfactory mechanical explanation could be found for electromagnetic phenomena. He would have argued:

Maxwell's theory describes electromagnetic waves and the laws of their propagation. This sentence alone shows that the explanation is of a mechanical nature. What is a wave? Think about a sound wave: it is produced by air particles. Thus, in a sound wave you have the mechanical picture of particles and their motion. Or think about water waves. Particles of water oscillate, forcing neighboring particles to oscillate too. This is how the waves spread or, rather, appear to spread. But the underlying reality is a mechanical one, of moving particles and the forces acting between them. The same is true for light waves or electromagnetic waves. Each simple electromagnetic wave can be described by a wave length, as in the case of water waves. By wave length, I mean the distance from a hilltop to the nearest hilltop at a given moment. The wave length of visible radiation, that is, of light, is small compared with the wave lengths of radio waves (even of short radio waves). But both for radio and light waves there is possible the mechanical picture of oscillating particles and a medium—the material background through which the waves travel.

We shall assume that our imaginary nineteenth-century physicist finishes his argument at this opportune moment and we ask him a question which ought to raise serious difficulties.

We argue: you said that the wave picture is of a mechanical character because there is always a medium, a material background through which the waves are propagated. Just what is the material background through which electromagnetic waves travel? Of course, not air, as in the case of a sound wave. There is no air at all between the stars and our earth. Pump the air out of this room and I, standing outside, would see through the windows exactly what I saw before. Air, water, or any other material medium is not involved in the propagation of electromagnetic waves. Unlike any other waves, they do not need a material background. This is precisely the characteristic feature that distinguishes them from any other waves. Where, then, is your mechanical background, if there is no material medium in which waves are propagated?

Of course, these arguments would not end the discussion. Our nineteenth-century physicist would defend his point of view and during such an argument one historically important word would appear: *ether*—a concept entirely superfluous for the understanding of modern physics; yet indispensable for the understanding of its history. For its failure gave birth to Einstein's relativity theory.

The physicist of the nineteenth century argued that because mechanical waves (and for him there weren't any other waves) can spread only in a material medium, then there must exist a material medium through which electromagnetic waves are propagated. This medium he called ether and assumed that our entire universe is immersed in this weightless substance of which he knew at least one property: that of transmitting electromagnetic waves. The same physicist would assure us that, given time, other properties would be discovered and the ether would become as real as any material object. Thus, his idea is that of two main branches of physics, but with the concept of the ether serving as a link between them, connecting the field theory with the mechanical theory and saving the cherished principle of unity.

Let us remember this picture and keep in mind how much effort went into forming, perfecting and justifying the concept of ether because only then shall we understand the revolution that destroyed the whole theoretical structure—the revolution that began when a young clerk in a patent office in Switzerland published a paper in the first years of our century.

THE FAILURE OF THE ETHER CONCEPT

In every exposition of relativity theory, one considers reference systems, or co-ordinate systems, or, as we shall say for short, *systems*. Such different *systems* are discussed both in the problems of mechanics and in field problems. But it was only the ether concept, and later relativity theory, which drew full attention to their importance. Many of the ether problems, and later many of the relativistic problems, are concerned with two or more *systems*.

Thus, in non-technical presentations it is helpful to think about experiments performed on the ground and then experiments performed, let us say, in a moving train. In all these examples our earth, and all stationary objects on it, form one *system* and the train forms another *system*. The two *systems* move relative to one another, and each *system* has its private observer or observers. Thus, there will be a group of men (as many as we need) performing experiments on the ground, and again observers experimenting in the train. These two teams of observers in both *systems* can compare notes with each other, if necessary, and will converse about their results. Some of our arguments will arise from such discussions. Indeed, if we may anticipate our story, this is one of the important methods of reasoning in relativity theory. The two *systems* are moving relative to each other; observers at work in their respective *systems* will find results that are valid relative to their *systems*; hence, the name—relativity theory.

We shall now formulate Galileo's relativity principle.

Imagine two *systems* in uniform motion relative to each other; that is, with constant, unaccelerated speed and along a straight line. If you wish to imagine the motion as that of a train, you must picture one in which the trunks do not overturn, in which passengers do not lurch against one another; or a ship that sails with such a delightful smoothness that even the most sensitive passengers do not become seasick. We do assume uniform motion!

Now we ask: are the laws of mechanics valid for the observers in both *systems* if they are valid in one of them? The answer is obvious: yes. Indeed, this is precisely what is implied by perfectly smooth motion. Cover the windows and there is no way of detecting such a uniform motion. Thus, if our observers compare notes on their physical experiments in the two *systems* they will find that they have formulated identical laws.

This is a simple concept and if we understand it then we understand, too, the meaning of Galileo's relativity principle. It says:

If the laws of mechanics are valid in any SYSTEM *then they are valid in any other* SYSTEM *in uniform motion relative to the original one.*

Any of these uniformly moving *systems* is as suitable for physical experiments as any other, and any one of them may be referred to in describing motions, velocities, accelerations, or forces.

The essential point is not that we have two or more *systems,* with observers in each of them, but that we can transfer the *description* from one *system* to another. All this is simple, but the simplicity is deceitful, for we shall soon discover that deep difficulties are hidden behind these seemingly trivial arguments.

A man tells me that his car travels at fifty miles per hour. If I wish to be pedantic, I may ask him, "Relative to what? To your house and the lamppost, or relative to the moon and the sun?" Questions of this sort are exasperating because, obviously, the man who was describing the speed of his car meant its speed relative to the earth or to objects (house, lamppost) rigidly connected with our earth. Motion can only be described relative to some reference system, and my interlocutor omitted the information only because it was obvious what *system* he was referring to.

When your train starts to move and a person runs after it, his speed relative to the station is considerable, although the speed relative to you is almost zero. If you run in your train with the speed *a*, and your train is travelling with the speed *b*, then your speed relative to the tracks is *a* plus *b*, or *a* minus *b*, depending upon which way you are running.

We shall now formulate the result in a more abstract manner. We have two *systems*: O (the ground) and O′ (the train). The *system* O′ moves with the speed *a* relative to O. A particle moves with the speed *b* relative to the *system* O′. To find the speed of this particle relative to the *system* O, you must add the two speeds if the particle moves in the same direction as O′ (relative to O) and subtract them if it moves in the opposite direction.

This rule, connecting the result of measurements of velocities in two *systems*, is both simple and obvious. So obvious, in deed, that it seems hardly worth while to confirm it by experiment. Yet, we may do so if we wish, and may repeat such an experiment as many times as we desire. Thus, we have a law to which we shall refer in the future as the *law of addition of velocities*.

We have just formulated:

1. Galileo's relativity principle
2. The law of addition of velocities

One more example before we leave these fundamental principles of the mechanical view: imagine that a man sitting in the middle of a long train delivers a lecture, or, putting it physically, he produces sound waves. We shall now ask an observer in the train and an observer outside the train the following question:

What is the speed of these sound waves in your *system*?

The observer in the train will say:

The speed of the sound waves is the same in all directions. The uniform motion of the train relative to the station does not matter. My *system* is just as good as that of the stationmaster. The train carries its own air with it and, therefore, the sound waves propagate with the same speed in all directions.

The observer outside will say:

The sound waves produced in the train move relative to me with different speeds in different directions. In the direction of the motion of the train they move with a speed greater than that of sound. In accordance with the classical law for adding velocities, such a speed will be that of the train plus that of the sound waves. In the direction opposite to the motion of the train, the sound spreads with smaller velocity. Indeed, this velocity relative to me will be smaller by the velocity of the train.

Let us remember these answers, for we shall have to refer to them soon.

Now, we can leave the mechanical theory and, under the guidance of the nineteenth-century physicist, start a series of investigations seeking to establish the reality of the ether. Our guide is determined to preserve the ether concept, unifying the mechanical and the field views. He would like the electromagnetic waves to be as real and as mechanical as sound waves.

Following our guide, whose ether theory we accept tentatively, we picture light waves simply as waves in the ether. To be concrete, we imagine that a flashlight, sending light signals, is turned on and off. If we prefer, we can think of radio signals instead, since both radio and light waves spread through ether with the same speed.

Thus, we are performing an experiment similar to that described before, in the case of sound waves. We investigate light signals sent from the middle of the long train and ask the observers inside and outside the train about the velocity of light relative to their *systems*. Of course, we may imagine that we can measure these velocities, but we prefer to ask our question before the observers have had an opportunity to do so. Let them predict and foresee the possible answers.

The observer in the train would say:

Obviously, my *system* is as good as the stationmaster's *system*. The windows of my train are closed and it is reasonable to assume that the ether is carried with my *system*, as the air was carried in the case of sound waves. Thus, the speed of light in my *system* will still be 186,000 miles per second, everywhere and in all directions.

The observer outside the train would say:

The velocity of this light signal will be different in different directions. It will be greater than normal in the direction of the train's motion relative to me. In this direction it will equal the sum of the normal velocity of light and the velocity of the train. In the opposite direction it will equal the normal velocity of light minus the velocity of the train.

Thus, the two men have made their predictions which can now be tested by experiment, from which there can be no further appeal in science.

If we were to perform this experiment, the prediction of the *outside* observer would prove unexpectedly wrong. True enough, the observer inside the train would find the velocity of light to be the same in all directions. His prediction would turn out to be correct, but the observer outside would be indisputably wrong. He would find that for him, too, the velocity of the light signal is the same in all directions, always 186,000 miles per second, never smaller or greater. He would find that for him light behaves as though its source and the ether were at rest; and the fact that the flashlight moves with the train is of no importance whatsoever. (The result of this theoretical experiment has been established indirectly although beyond dispute by scientific observations.) Thus, experiment pronounces its verdict: the velocity of light is the same for the inside and outside observer.

Thus, the law of addition of velocities has broken down. What advantage is there, then, in assuming the existence of an ether if it does not act as a proper medium should; if, instead of helping us to predict events, it leads to new difficulties? The ether, which ought to have linked the field and the mechanical theories, has violated mechanics by violating the law of addition of velocities.

Deeply rooted prejudices die hard. The physicist of the nineteenth century was not prepared to sacrifice the ether concept. He could not deny the evidence of experiment, but he could change his argument. Indeed, he might hit upon a plausible explanation for his failure. He might say, and he has said: the train does not carry the ether, as it does the medium of air, but instead it floats through the ether sea like a ship floating through calm waters; the earth, too, in its journey around the sun, drifts through this calm ether sea. Thus, our former picture was wrong and we must start the experiment all over again, again asking our observers to predict the results and compare their predictions with experiments. In doing this, we are nearing the climax of our story. Again there are two observers, the one outside in the calm ether sea, and the one floating through the calm ether sea. Once again we register predictions, but now, to be more consistent, we have changed our picture slightly. We imagine one observer connected not with the earth but with some *system*—let us say the sun or the stars, perhaps: *the system* in which the ether sea is at rest. *This system* is the only one in which ether rests, and all other bodies float relative to it. The "universal" observer—that is, the observer for whom the ether is at rest—would say:

For me the velocity of light is the same in all directions because the medium through which light waves travel is at rest.

What about the observer who floats through such an ether sea? Imagine that he does so in a moving system such as a train, and that, as before, he sends a signal in the direction of the motion and a signal in the opposite direction. He would now say:

If I send a signal—that is, a light wave—in the direction of the train's motion, then the light wave moves through the immobile ether sea, but the wall toward which the wave moves runs away from this wave. The opposite wall moves toward the wave. Thus, the two walls will not be met by the light signals simultaneously. The escaping wall will be met later; the opposite wall will be met first by the light waves. Consequently, the velocity of light will not be the same in both directions. It will be smaller than the normal velocity of light toward the escaping wall, greater than the normal velocity of light toward the opposite wall. Let us call the normal velocity of light *c*; that is, *c* stands for 186,000 miles per second. For me the velocity of light will be smaller than *c* in the direction of motion and greater than *c* in the opposite direction.

These are clear predictions. Before we test them experimentally, let us pause for a moment to emphasize the importance of the picture we have sketched.

According to this new picture, there is one, and only one, *system* in which the ether is at rest. Such a *system* is distinguished from all others. It is, as we said, *the system*. Thus, we are trapped in our own arguments. In trying to formulate a concept of ether that would unify the mechanical and the field theories, the physicist who accepts the ether concept is forced to undermine the mechanical theory itself. He is ready to sacrifice Galileo's relativity principle, a very essential part of the mechanical view. For Galileo's relativity principle states that all *systems* in uniform motion relative to each other are equivalent. But this is not so according to the physicist who believes in ether. Among the *systems*, there is one distinguished before all others, *the system* in which the ether is at rest, the one and only one in which the speed of light is *c*. Thus, Galileo's relativity principle can no longer hold true. The ether replaces it by an absolute theory. While trying to save the mechanical view, the nineteenth-century physicist has jeopardized it by abandoning its basic principle of relativity.

What does experiment say? All our astronomical observations indicate clearly that if there is a resting ether sea, then our earth, in its journey around the sun, moves relative to it. Thus, our example of the train floating through the ether is well represented by our earth moving with the velocity of about twenty miles per second around the sun. Consequently, on our earth the velocity of light in the direction of the motion of our earth should be slightly smaller than the velocity in the opposite direction. The famous Michelson-Morley experiment performed in 1887 was designed to detect such a difference. The result was negative. It proved conclusively that there are no different velocities of light! They are the same in all directions and their value is *c*, the speed of light, which strangely enough always remains true to itself, always constant, always unchangeable.

For the mechanist the result is catastrophic. The concept of the ether, which gave promise of unifying the mechanical and the field views, has led to inevitable inconsistencies. An ether that neither moves nor rests, which is neither carried by bodies nor allows bodies to flow through it, is a dismal fiasco. All attempts to look upon ether as a material background for waves have failed completely and we are again faced with two seemingly contradictory branches of physics without any unifying concept.

As I have said, scientific prejudices die hard. The desire to invent a medium for the propagation of electromagnetic waves was so strong that even after it was proved that ether neither rests nor moves, attempts were still made to hold on to the concept of an ether by introducing new assumptions, which made the structure of theoretical physics more complicated, more artificial, and less convincing.

Let us glance once more at the state of physics, or rather its foundations at the beginning of this century.

The mechanical view accepted:
The Galileo relativity principle and
The rule of adding velocities.

Experiments on light and electromagnetic waves led us to the conclusion that:

The velocity of electromagnetic waves, or light, is always the same, and it does not matter whether the source or the observer moves.

The last result was inconsistent with the concept of ether. Moreover, it was inconsistent with the rule of adding velocities. The velocity of light, together with the velocity of a *system*, results in the unchanged velocity of light!

Not only did the ether concept collapse but the mechanical and the field view contradicted each other. Experiments had revealed apparently irremovable inconsistencies in the scientific picture of the external world.

Physics was ripe for the Einstein revolution.

What do we mean by a revolution in physics? We mean: a sudden clarification of our concepts, the forming of a new picture, an unexpected resolution of contradictions and difficulties. There have been many revolutions in science, but the Einstein revolution became the most famous. Among its results is one that for years to come will form an important factor in shaping life and death on our planet.

CHAPTER THREE

THE FIRST EINSTEIN REVOLUTION

ONE AND TWO BUT NOT THREE

ANNALEN DER PHYSIK is a German journal, bound in fat volumes full of scientific papers, usually very technical and erudite, and richly peppered with footnotes and references. The seventeenth volume of *Annalen der Physik,* printed in 1905, contains Einstein's thirty-page paper "On the Electrodynamics of Moving Bodies." The title sounds modest, yet as we read it we notice almost immediately that it is different from other papers. There are no references; no authorities are quoted, and the few footnotes are of an explanatory character. The style is simple, and a great part of this article can be followed without advanced technical knowledge. But its full understanding requires a maturity of mind and taste that is more rare and precious than pedantic knowledge, for Einstein's paper deals with the most basic problems; it analyzes the meanings of concepts that might seem too simple to be scrutinized.

Recently when I reread Einstein's paper, I was once more struck by its finished form. Even today, his presentation and style have lost nothing of their freshness. It is still the best source from which to learn relativity theory.

In the second section of Einstein's paper we read:

1. The laws according to which the states of a physical system change do not depend on which of the two coordinate systems, in uniform relative motion, these laws refer to.

2. Every light ray moves in a "rest" co-ordinate system with a definite speed *c*, whether emitted from a stationary or a moving source.

These are the foundations on which relativity theory is built. They are simple assumptions, both based on experience. As we shall discover, the solution of our difficulties is gained by accepting the inevitable. As in a good mystery story, it is the most obvious solution that we have consistently refused to accept.

But if we wish to understand relativity theory, we must fully understand these assumptions on which it is based. Everything else is logical deduction and there can be no more in the deduced results than in the hypotheses from which they follow.

The first assumption is a restatement of Galileo's relativity principle, which we have described in the preceding chapter. It postulates that all laws of nature are the same in two *systems* in uniform relative motion; that neither through mechanical nor through electromagnetic phenomena shall we detect uniform motion. The nineteenth-century physicist thought that there was an ether and that *the system* in which such an ether was at rest was distinguished from all others. But this assumption was clearly contradicted by experiment, and Einstein suggests that we accept the verdict of experiment without further appeal. Whether we are investigating mechanical or electromagnetic phenomena, they are all governed by the relativity principle: there is no way of distinguishing between *two systems* in relative uniform motion. But, if this is true, then the ether concept can be shown to be superfluous. It has created enough confusion, and there is no way of detecting its presence. It did not bring the laws governing electromagnetic phenomena into the theoretical framework of classical mechanics; its structure proved too fantastic and too artificial to form any real connection between these two branches of physics.

Thus, we can describe Einstein's achievement as destroying once and for all the concept of ether which had been invented to unite the field laws and the laws of mechanics. But, in doing so, he did not sever the connection between these two realms of physics; on the contrary, he brought them nearer together. For now we have a unifying concept in the physical content of Galileo's relativity principle which governs both the mechanical and field phenomena.

We turn to the second basic assumption of special relativity. It is equally simple and merely states explicitly that the speed of light is always the same, irrespective of what *system* we measure it in: whether we measure it inside the train or outside.

We may feel disappointed. Where, then, is the great Einstein revolution? These two principles are merely a formulation of experimental results, and all that Einstein seems to have done is to accept the inevitable. Where, then, lies the originality of Einstein's theory?

The next step in our argument is important. In spite of the simplicity of Einstein's fundamental assumptions, taken together they are revolutionary. Until Einstein's time, these two principles had seemed to contradict each other. Einstein removed the contradiction, but in doing this he was forced to change our most basic concepts of space and time.

The two principles seemed to contradict each other inevitably. For if the speed of light in a moving train is c, then how can it also be c outside? Shouldn't it be greater in the direction of motion of the train and smaller in the opposite direction? Or, reversing the argument, if the speed of light for the observer outside the train is c, then shouldn't it be different inside? Before relativity theory, it seemed impossible to escape such a conclusion, following as it did from a time-honored chapter of mechanics on combining velocities in two different *systems*. The simple principle of a constant light velocity contradicts the equally simple principle of adding or subtracting velocities, of combining the velocity of light (or any other velocity) with the velocity of the *system*.

For the sake of clarity, we shall write out the three principles:

One: Relativity principle
Two: Constancy of the velocity of light
Three: Addition of velocities

We cannot accept all of them. We must reject *Two* if we wish to accept *One* and *Three*. Einstein's solution was: accept *One* and *Two* and draw your own conclusions. You will see that to do this *Three* cannot be accepted as rigorously valid. Therefore, it *is not* rigorously valid, and experiment will show that it is not. We must build a new physics, based on the fundamental assumptions *One* and *Two*. Indeed, such a physics can be built, a physics logically consistent and consistent with experiment; a new relativistic physics to which the old Newtonian physics becomes only an approximation, useful and valid for bodies moving with speeds small compared to that of light, but invalid if the velocities of moving bodies approach that of light. Thus, when we are considering cars or supersonic planes, or even the planets of our solar system, we can still employ the principles of classical mechanics; but if we are dealing with electrons moving with speeds, say, only ten per cent smaller than that of light, Newtonian mechanics breaks down and a new mechanics, the Einstein relativistic mechanics, must be used. It is not quite correct to say that Einstein has proven Newtonian mechanics to be inapplicable. It is more correct to say that he has shown its limitations. But the region in which it works is still vast; and for a long time it will continue to be taught in our schools and applied to our everyday life.

THE MOVING CLOCK

To build a consistent physics based on Einstein's two principles, we must radically revise our fundamental concepts of space and time. It is almost unbelievable that these basic, intuitive concepts have never before been defined in physics. They were mistakenly regarded as being too obvious to require clarification or analysis. Yet, if we try to define them, we immediately encounter unanticipated difficulties, which are resolved only in Einstein's relativity theory.

The simple question that Einstein raised and answered is: What is the meaning of the phrase "two simultaneous events"? Though at that time (1905) physics had become quite sophisticated, the concept of two simultaneous events seemed so unambiguous that no one before Einstein bothered to scrutinize it. Einstein did just this, starting his analysis with the simplest sentence I have ever encountered in a scientific paper:

> All our judgments in which time plays a role are judgments about simultaneous events. If I say, for example, "the train arrives here at 7," this means: the coincidence of the small hand of my watch with the number 7 and the arrival of the train are simultaneous events.

Here we have given a meaning to a very simple situation of two simultaneous events (coincidence of the small hand of the watch with the number 7 and the train's arrival), occurring in each other's neighborhood. But what does it mean to assert that two events in New York and San Francisco are simultaneous events? Now the question becomes more difficult and we must reflect a little before answering it. The simplest reply would be that the two events are simultaneous if two clocks, one in New York, the other in San Francisco, show that they are simultaneous. This answer may prove all right after we have added a few qualifications. First, we must know that they are both good clocks, and, to simplify matters, we can assume that they are of the same structure or, as we shall say, identical clocks. It is not so easy to say what a good clock is, but let us skip this difficulty since no great danger lies in ignoring it. Of course, if one of them should indicate Eastern Time and the other Pacific Time, two events would not be simultaneous when these clocks show the same time. They must not only have the same rhythm, but they must simultaneously show the same time or, as we say briefly, they must be *synchronized*. What does it mean to state that two clocks are synchronized? Imagine that it is exactly seven o'clock in New York and we send a radio signal telling an observer in San Francisco to put his clock at seven. If he does this, will the two clocks then be synchronized? Not exactly. The radio signal travels with a great but finite speed—that of light. Thus, if the observer in San Francisco receives the signal that it is seven, he must set his clock at some time slightly after seven: to be exact, seven plus the time the signal took to travel between these two cities.

We can, however, imagine a simple experiment telling us whether the two clocks, in these two cities, are synchronized or not. Imagine a point exactly half way between New York and San Francisco. At this place, we look at a television picture of the two clocks. If, in this picture, these two clocks show the same time at every moment, then they are synchronized. Then, and only then, are they able to be used to determine simultaneous events. Similarly, we can now imagine synchronized clocks spread over the entire globe. Any two of them will give us identical television pictures at a point midway between them.

Only now, with all these stipulations, can we judge whether two events at two different places are simultaneous or not. If an event occurred in New York at seven o'clock and in San Francisco at seven o'clock, as judged by a pair of these synchronized clocks, then these can be described as two simultaneous events. But our analysis of simultaneity is not finished. All that we have asserted up to this point about two simultaneous events is just as true in classical mechanics as in relativity theory. Classical physics did not bother to formulate these assumptions because it seemed that little would be gained by such a scrupulous analysis.

The divergence between classical and relativistic concepts of simultaneity is apparent only if we consider simultaneous events in two *systems*. We have described how crucial it is in relativity theory to consider two different *systems* and allow observers in both of them to discuss the results of experiments they have performed. Thus, we should now think of two *systems*, say, the earth with its stationary objects and a moving train. Each observer on the earth has as many synchronized clocks as are needed to determine the time of events at different places, and the observer on the train has his own synchronized clocks too. Each *system* then has its private synchronized clocks to judge the times at which events occur.

Now comes the essential point. Imagine two events. We can think of two very simple ones, such as two light signals, sent at different times from two different points in space. A flashlight is turned on and off at a certain moment at a certain point in space: this is one event. Now we consider two such events and ask whether they are simultaneous or not. Suppose that the observer on the earth does find that these two events are simultaneous as judged by his clocks. What about the observer in the train? Will he find them simultaneous too?

This is a crucial question. It is here that the answers of classical physics and relativity theory differ radically. As we shall see, relativity theory, by defining the concept of simultaneity rigorously for the first time, drew from it new conclusions essential to the further development of science.

The classical physicist would answer:

Of course, two events simultaneous in one *system* (earth) are simultaneous in another *system* (train). I allowed you to use different clocks at different points and even different clocks in different *systems*. I agreed with your definition of synchronization and accepted it fully, but none of this can change my conclusion that two events, simultaneous in one *system*, are simultaneous in another. Clocks do not change their rhythm when they move! It matters little whether you consult a resting clock or a moving clock, or whether the observers use private clocks resting in either *system* or universal clocks for all the *systems*. As Newton has said, time is absolute and that means precisely that time does not change from one *system* to another, and that we can use one set of clocks for all *systems*. Time flows uniformly for all observers. Thus, two events simultaneous in one *system* must be simultaneous in another. There is not a shred of evidence that clocks change their rhythm while in motion. Start a quick journey at Southampton and the clock on the ship will show the same time as the clock in New York if the two clocks were synchronized at the beginning of the journey.

Thus the classical physicist insists that time is absolute, that the moving clock does not change its rhythm. Here the relativist would ask a simple question:

"How do you know that a clock does not change its rhythm while in motion?"

Empty and prolonged arguments in physics are rare. Soon the inner consistency of a theory and the evidence of experiment will lead to a final verdict. To appeal from it to common sense is misleading, since the pronouncement of common sense on such a question may reflect only a universal prejudice, which will not stand up under rigorous scrutiny and which must then be uprooted if the progress of scientific thought is to be assured. In the long run an appeal to an authority, even as high as Newton's, will be of little help either. Newton's theories were consistent in his time, for science in the Newtonian age was not ripe for relativity theory. The assumption of absolute time did not lead to contradictions when applied to facts known up to the nineteenth century. Indeed, it would have been futile to assume that the clock on its journey from Southampton to New York changes its rhythm. No experiment could detect such a change. But what would happen if the same ship were to travel with a speed only slightly smaller than that of light? Would the rhythm of such a clock still remain unchanged? In the early nineteenth century this would have been a purely academic question, but it is not today. Nowadays, we can force particles to move with a speed only slightly smaller than that of light.

We return to our question:

"Does a moving clock change its rhythm while in motion?"

Yes, answers relativity theory. Two events, simultaneous in one *system,* are not simultaneous in another, and there is *no absolute time.* That the concept of time is relative is a necessary assumption for the inner consistency of our theory and for its agreement with experiment.

Here we have arrived at an essential point in our argument. We have seen now where the classical and relativistic developments diverge. The concept of time is changed; a subject on which volumes were written by philosophers has been changed by considerations arising in the field of physics.

The relativistic character of time and of the concept of simultaneity can be deduced from the two fundamental assumptions of relativity theory: (1) the equivalence of *systems* in relative uniform motion and (2) the constancy of the velocity of light.

We shall now explain why the absolute character of simultaneity must be sacrificed if these two assumptions of relativity theory are accepted.

From the middle of a train (moving *system*) let us send, at one instant, two light rays in opposite directions. Since the speed of light (c) is constant for the inside observer, in his *system* these two light rays will reach the two opposite walls at the same time and for him these two events (the light rays striking the two opposite walls) will be simultaneous. What about the observer outside (on the earth)? For him, too, the speed of light is still the constant c in his *system*; but, looking at the train, he sees that one wall moves away from the light and the opposite wall moves toward the light. Thus, for him one light ray will first strike the wall that moves toward it and sometime later the light ray will strike the wall that moves away from it. This leads to the inevitable conclusion that two events simultaneous for observers in one *system* are not simultaneous for the observers in a second *system* moving uniformly relative to the first.

Here, indeed, is a revolution in our habits of thinking and in our use of language. A sentence, "Two events occurred at the same time," is meaningless if we don't specify, or at least imply clearly, the *system* to which we are referring. The difference in judgment between the inside and outside observer (train-earth) must be attributable to their employing different clocks, since both *systems* have their own private clocks. We conclude that a moving clock changes its rhythm while in motion.

GALILEO AND LORENTZ

We cannot go much further without the use of mathematics. What Einstein did was to express his two postulates in a rigorous mathematical form which enabled him to draw new conclusions. It would not be too difficult to follow Einstein's reasoning, but it would require the use of mathematical technique, and at some point of such an investigation those who are familiar with such a technique and those who are not must part. For those who are not, deduction must cease and all that can be done is to explain the results of such mathematical deductions in terms of our ordinary language.

We shall, however, be obliged to use a term which can be fully understood only with the help of mathematics. We shall not define rigorously but introduce rather vaguely this important term in relativity theory: *the Lorentz transformation.* It forms the pillar on which relativity theory rests.

To form an idea of how the Lorentz transformation is used, let us consider, as before, the situation of two *systems* in uniform relative motion. For a concrete picture of this, imagine, for example, a bus speeding along Fifth Avenue. The bus is four blocks long, very narrow, and we can let it travel with any speed we wish so long as it moves uniformly. The position of any observer at rest in this bus can be denoted by one number (the bus, remember, is very narrow), representing the distance from its center, and we shall call the distance positive in the direction of motion and negative in the other. If we wish to employ the terminology of mathematics, we can say that every observer or every particle has a *co-ordinate* representing its position in the bus, relative to the bus. Now, for the outside observer standing on Fifth Avenue, the center of the bus changes its position with time. Relative to the rigid frame of the blocks of Fifth Avenue, the position of the center of the bus will now be Forty-second Street, then Sixty-ninth Street, and so on. If the position of the center of the bus is at Forty-second Street, the position of the driver will be at Forty-fourth Street and the position of the last passenger, at Fortieth Street, since the bus is four blocks long. All this is simple and it means that we can find the co-ordinates of any observer in the bus relative to the Fifth Avenue *system* at any moment if we know the co-ordinate of the observer relative to the bus, if we know the speed of the bus, and if we know from where and when the bus started. In scientific language we have, according to classical mechanics: the co-ordinate in the Fifth Avenue *system* equals the speed of the bus multiplied by the time of travel plus the co-ordinate in the bus *system*.

Suppose that an event happens in the bus, such as the flashing of a light signal. To describe this event, we must know when and where it happened. We need to use for its description two numbers, one of them denoting the space, the other denoting the time co-ordinate. Whereas the space co-ordinate will be different for the observer on Fifth Avenue and in the bus, the other number, denoting time will be, *according to classical mechanics,* the same for all observers since time is absolute and a clock does not change its rhythm while in motion. Thus, knowing the co-ordinates of space and time of an event in one *system* and the relative speed of these two *systems,* we can find the space and time co-ordinates in the other *system.* The rule for the space co-ordinate was stated before; the rule for the time co-ordinate is very simple: the time co-ordinates are the same. Thus, two *systems* moving uniformly relative to each other, two *systems* in which the laws of physics are the same, are connected with each other in classical physics by what we call a *Galileo transformation,* a rule that allows us to find co-ordinates of events in one *system* if they are known in the other.

What relativity theory claims or, rather, what it deduces from its two principles is that the Galileo transformation is not valid. We can state this more suitably by saying that it is practically valid if the relative speeds are very small compared with the speed of light. It breaks down completely if the relative velocities approach that of light. Thus, we may use classical mechanics and the Galileo transformation while talking about cars, supersonic planes, even rockets, while, in effect, we are dealing with the phenomena of classical mechanics. But, in the rapidly expanding field of modern atomic physics, for example, where nature or technique frequently provides us with velocities that are not small compared with the velocity of light, the Galileo transformation fails and it has to be replaced by the Lorentz transformation. The Lorentz transformation does successfully what the Galileo transformation fails to do for such speeds. It provides us with a means of finding the space and time co-ordinates of events in one *system* if they are known in the other, and if the relative speed of these two *systems* is known. What is the essential difference between the Galileo and the Lorentz transformation? Whereas in the Galileo transformation the time co-ordinate of an event is the same for all *systems,* it is not the same in the Lorentz transformation. The rhythm of the clock changes in accordance with the relativity of time, and two simultaneous events in one *system* are not simultaneous in another. It wouldn't be correct to say that the Lorentz transformation works well for great velocities while the Galileo transformation applies to small velocities. It would be more correct to say that the Lorentz transformation is always valid. For small velocities, there are no practical differences between the Galileo and the Lorentz transformations, but these differences become important and accessible to experimental verification when the speeds approach that of light.

We shall not write down the Lorentz transformation, although a knowlege of algebra would suffice to interpret it. It is enough to assert that this transformation connects in a new way the space and time co-ordinates of an event in one *system* with time and space co-ordinates of the same event in another, and that this connection can be deduced from the two fundamental assumptions that Einstein formulated in his famous paper. Such a transformation carries us over from one *system* to another, if both are moving uniformly relative to each other. Since the laws of nature in two such *systems* are the same, we may say that it is the Lorentz and not the Galileo transformation that leaves the laws of physics unchanged.

Thus, a revolution took place; a new and powerful principle was born, a general theoretical framework into which all the laws of nature must be fitted. If any new law is formulated, we now ask: does this law satisfy the principle of relativity theory? That is, is the law the same for all *systems* in uniform relative motion? Or, mathematically: is this law unchangeable under the Lorentz transformation (which recognizes the relative character not only of space but also of time)? If we apply such a criterion to the laws of Maxwell's theory, as Einstein did in his paper, we see that Maxwell's theory governing the phenomena of electromagnetic waves is a permissible theory because it satisfies the principle of *invariance*; that is, because the structure of Maxwell's equations does not change under the Lorentz transformation.

What about Newtonian mechanics? No, it is not invariant under the Lorentz transformation; it is invariant only under the Galileo transformation. Thus, a new mechanics had to be built: a mechanics that would apply to particles moving with great speeds, and which would be invariant with respect to the Lorentz transformation. This new physics satisfying the new principle of relativity theory, the principle of invariance with respect to the Lorentz transformation, was built by Einstein in his famous paper published in 1905. Two main branches of physics, the mechanical and the field theories, became connected, not by the assumption of an ether, but by the new Einstein relativity principle, which both the mechanical and field view must satisfy, and classical mechanics emerges as a good and useful approximation to the new mechanics, when the speeds are small compared with that of light.

This new relativistic frame became one of the most important guides in modern physics. The harvest of Einstein's ideas in this century was one of the richest that any man has ever brought to science. From relativity theory as formulated in 1905, a road forward was possible, and much of it was later traversed under the leadership of Einstein. A retreat into the old positions in classical physics has become unthinkable. The impact of relativity theory upon the entire development of modern physics cannot be exaggerated; but its impact is not limited to modern physics alone, for relativity theory has influenced our whole modern life. It has already influenced our philosophical views on space and time, and it will surely influence the technological development of the future.

ONE PRINCIPLE INSTEAD OF TWO

Why have we referred to the velocity of light or a velocity smaller than that of light but never to a velocity greater than that of light? The reason is that, according to relativity theory, there can be no velocity greater than that of light. According to classical mechanics, if a particle moves with some velocity in the Fifth Avenue bus, then its velocity relative to the outside observer is equal to its velocity relative to the bus plus the velocity of the bus. Thus any velocity can be increased. But, as we have seen, the classical law of adding velocities is inconsistent with the assumptions upon which relativity theory is based. Indeed, if light travels with the velocity *c,* relative to the bus, then its velocity relative to the outside—that is, the Fifth Avenue observer—will still be the constant *c,* no matter how slowly or quickly the bus moves. The classical law of addition of velocities must be changed and this change can be deduced from the Lorentz transformation which replaces the classical Galileo transformation.

There is one important deduction from relativity theory which Einstein mentions in his first paper and to which he returns later in a short paper appearing in the next volume of *Annalen der Physik.* Its title is "Does the Inertia of a Body Depend on Its Energy?" If I were to say that the ideas expressed in this paper were world-shaking, I would not be exaggerating, since here for the first time we find a theoretical formulation of a possible new phenomenon which has opened boundless vistas into the field of science and the technology of war and peace. This short paper states: the use of atomic energy is, in principle, possible. Forty years later, the work of many scientists showed that the use of atomic energy is practicable, as was demonstrated in a form as clear as the photographs of the explosion in the New Mexican desert and the devastation at Hiroshima. Ironically enough, the seeds for the future utilization of atomic energy were sown by the most peaceful man in the world, by a lonely man who abhors violence and has contempt for brute force.

Einstein showed that the use of atomic energy is theoretically possible, but no one, including Einstein, knew whether or not it would some day be practically possible. This knowledge was gained only recently, and one could equally well imagine that the answer might have been that the use of atomic energy was only theoretically possible. Then Einstein's name would not have been linked with an atomic bomb and very little with technology. Yet, his name would have been just as important in the history of our civilization. The creation of relativity theory means the birth of modern physics; it brought a deep change in our basic philosophic ideas and a thorough revision of the foundations on which modern science is built.

The end of Einstein's short paper contains the following lines:

> The mass of a body is a measure of its energy. If its energy changes by L, then its mass changes by $L/9.10^{20}$, if energy is measured in ergs and mass in grams.
>
> Is it not possible that for bodies with an energy content changeable in a high degree (for example, the radium salts) a test of such a theory may succeed?

In these words, not only is an important conclusion drawn from relativity theory, but also the possibility of its verification is predicted.

Can such a conclusion be deduced from the two abstract principles on which this theory is based? It can, for no new principle enters the picture.

Let us divide our task of explaining this fundamental deduction into two parts: first, we wish to set forth its full implications; later, we shall examine its connection with the assumptions of relativity theory.

The classical physicist of the nineteenth century believed in two laws of conservation: (1) the law of conservation of mass; (2) the law of conservation of energy. The law of conservation of mass maintains that you may heat a body, deform it, change it chemically, but the total mass will remain the same. Energy, on the other hand, is something that will do work but has no mass. In a steam engine, for example, heat changes into work, but mass does not enter the picture, for, according to classical physics, heat has neither weight nor mass. The sun sends radiation into space, a small fraction of which falls upon our earth, carrying with it the energy of radiation which changes into heat or into the chemical energy stored by plants. But this radiation does not carry mass either. Thus we have, side by side, two different quantities, mass and energy. They appear to the classical physicists as something distinct both qualitatively and quantitatively. Mass is measured in grams while energy, like work, is measured in ergs. (An erg equals the work done by the force of one dyne along the distance of one centimeter. One dyne is the force that accelerates one gram by one centimetre per second per second. All this constitutes a technical definition. It is sufficient to know that an erg is a small unit of work and energy.) If you heat a glass of water, its temperature and its amount of heat change. Does the mass of this glass of water change? The classical physicist would claim that it does not.

But relativity theory leads to an entirely different answer. It deduces that energy is not weightless, but has a definite mass. If the amount of energy changes, so does its mass. Energy has mass and mass has energy. There are not two principles of conservation. There is only one, and that is the principle of conservation of mass-energy. Mass and energy are as different as cents and dollars, but just as you can change cents into dollars and vice versa, so at least in principle can you change mass into energy and energy into mass. Relativity theory provides this rate of exchange. It is the fact that this rate of exchange is extremely low that kept the one principle of conservation hidden from science and made energy appear weightless, thus perpetuating the use of two principles instead of one.

The change in mass predicted by relativity theory when you heat a glass of water is indeed so small that it could not be detected by weighing on the most sensitive scales. Imagine that you add to a glass of water or to any other system some ergs of energy. How many grams does such energy weigh, or by how many grams did you increase your original mass? The answer is: by very little indeed. It is even less than if we added one devaluated drachma to the bank account of a dollar-millionaire. The energy represents an extremely devaluated currency compared to the mass as expressed in grams. But a currency it is, a fluid currency which can be used for work. Mass is stored in a highly valuable currency which only now are we learning to use by changing its tremendous and formerly inaccessible stores into the fluent but highly devaluated currency of energy. Thus, the rate of exchange between the high currency of mass and the devaluated currency of energy is given by a very great number: one gram equals 900,000,000,000,000,000,000 ergs!

Measured in ergs, one gram equals the speed of light times the speed of light, if this velocity is expressed in centimeters per second. (Expressed this way, the velocity of light equals 30,000,000,000 centimetres per second.)

Thus, the mass of energy, in grams, is obtained by dividing this energy in ergs by the tremendous number we have cited. To give an example: the quantity of heat needed to convert one thousand tons of water entirely into steam would weigh not quite one-thirtieth of a gram. It is because of this negligible mass of energy that it was for such a long time regarded as weightless.

To summarize: relativity theory rejects the distinction between mass and energy. Each unit of mass represents an enormous store of energy and each unit of energy possesses a very small mass. The two principles of conservation, those of mass and energy, were combined by relativity theory into one, which we may call the principle of conservation either of mass or energy. The rate of exchange between these two quantities is established, and the two concepts, mass and energy, are unified. They are two words for the same underlying reality.

How does the relation between mass and energy proceed from the assumptions of relativity theory? Although we cannot deduce this result here, we have already covered enough ground to make Einstein's great deduction plausible.

The foundations of classical mechanics lie in Newton's law of motion. To change a velocity, to produce an acceleration, force is needed. On the other hand, mass, as we said, is regarded in classical mechanics as something constant and unchangeable. If you wish to increase the velocity of a given mass by one metre per second, you must exert a specific force, and it does not make the slightest difference if your velocity is zero or very near to that of light. It is not the velocity that matters, but the acceleration. The greater the mass, the greater is the inertia, or the resistance of the body to the acceleration. This fact is as simple and familiar as the fact that it is harder to accelerate a big stone than a small stone. According to classical physics, inertia (that is, mass) does not change with speed. It is just as easy or just as difficult to increase the speed by one metre per second when the body moves with the speed of light as it is when the same body is at rest. This obviously cannot be so according to relativity theory, which does not admit speeds greater than that of light. But then, to explain the impossibility of unlimited acceleration, we must deduce that mass increases with velocity! Indeed, if the speed is very near to that of light, the inertial mass must be so great that no force can make the velocity greater than that of light. According to relativity theory, the mass must become infinitely great as the speed of the body approaches that of light! How otherwise could we interpret the fact that no body can be accelerated to a velocity greater than that of light?

According to classical physics, mass is unchangeable and does not depend on speed; but it is changeable and does depend on speed in relativity theory. We know not only the qualitative but also the quantitative law of such a change.

According to classical physics, a moving body has kinetic energy just because it moves. This energy, like all energy, is weightless, or let us say the same thing differently: the mass of a moving body does not change.

But in relativity theory mass must change with speed, or, to put it differently, kinetic energy must have mass, however small. And the rate of exchange between mass and kinetic energy is exactly the same as quoted before: the rate that connected the devaluated energy currency with the hard mass currency. Einstein also showed that the fundamental mass-energy relation is true not only for kinetic energy but for every kind of energy.

We see how far the ramifications of relativity theory spread. Since we started our exposition we have covered much ground and we can now see a new physics emerging in the deductions from its basic assumptions. The groundwork of this new physics was established by Einstein with great clarity in two papers—

and in fewer pages than are used here to indicate some of the results.

"A PARADOX? A PARADOX! A MOST INGENIOUS PARADOX!"

From the time Einstein was fifteen or sixteen years old (so he has often told me) he puzzled over the question: what will happen if a man tries to catch a light ray? For years he thought about this very problem. Its solution led to relativity theory. We see in this one example some important features of Einstein's genius. First, and above all, there is the capacity for wonder. Secondly, there is the ability to think for years about the same problem, until darkness changes into the light of understanding. And thirdly, there is the ability to formulate simple, ideal experiments, experiments that can never be performed in practice but experiments which, if properly analyzed, clarify and change our understanding of the world around us.

Indeed, in the case of a man who catches and runs with a light ray we see the great puzzle that led to relativity theory. For such a man, because he moves uniformly, all phenomena should be the same as for the man who stands still; but, on the other hand, he always remains in front of the light wave, and for him light stands still. Something would appear to oscillate but the wave would not spread. Relativity theory and the rejection of Galileo's transformation is the answer to this puzzle. No material body can travel as fast as light. For every observer the speed of light will remain the constant value c. No man can successfully chase a light ray.

Since we now realize the importance of simultaneity in relativity theory, let us look closer at the concept of clocks changing their rhythm and consider other conclusions that can be drawn from it. We return to the example of the bus racing along Fifth Avenue. If at some moment during the journey the bus driver finds that his clock shows the same time as the nearest clock outside, he will find out later that his clock differs from the many Fifth Avenue clocks that he passes; the rhythm of his clock is slower, and the greater the speed, the slower will be the rhythm. The moving clock would stand still if the velocity of the bus were that of light. But let us remember: we compare the rhythm of *one* clock in the bus with the rhythm of *many* clocks on Fifth Avenue.

That the above conclusion can be deduced from relativity theory, and more specifically from the Lorentz transformation, seemed so fantastic that people began to joke about it, convinced that relativity theory must be nonsensical if such conclusions could be drawn from it. These objections were often formulated in the form of the *twin paradox*. Imagine that identical twins are born on Fifth Avenue and one is placed in our Fifth Avenue bus, while the other is kept on the street. Now the bus travels with great speed and a clock moving with it has a slow rhythm compared with the Fifth Avenue clocks. We can imagine that Fifth Avenue leads far into stellar space, that one of the twins starts the journey with a velocity near to that of light, and that the voyage into space is a long one. Now the heart of our twin in the bus can be thought of as a clock, and it beats in a very slow rhythm compared with all the human hearts it passes. Somewhere, far away, the bus stops and returns to earth. On its journey back it again saves time because the slowing up of the rhythm depends only on the speed and not on the direction of motion. (We assume that away from the earth and toward the earth the motion is uniform. The only non-uniformity happens when the bus turns around, but the influence of such non-uniform motion can be assumed as small as we wish because we can go as far as we like and save as much time as we please.) Thus, the twin returns to the other twin. But because of relativity theory the one that travelled is in his prime, has all his teeth and all his hair, whereas the other is an old man nearing the grave. The two identical twins will look quite different according to relativity theory, for what we have said is a conclusion from its two principles. What is the answer to the paradox of the two identical twins?

It was thrown again and again into the face of relativity theory to show how absurd are its conclusions. But actually they do not contradict experience, but only our traditional notions of absolute time. We have never been able to perform such an experiment, but if we could, the answer would, I believe, be precisely what relativity theory predicts.

Yet it would be convincing to have a direct experiment showing that a moving clock does change its rhythm. There is a tremendous amount of evidence for relativity theory but of rather an indirect type. Direct experimental verification is not easy because, as always in relativity theory, any differences between classical mechanics and relativity theory are detectable only if the speeds approach that of light. Yet, in 1938, long after relativity theory was formulated, an interesting experiment, showing directly the change of rhythm with velocity, was performed by Ives. The experiment involved the hydrogen atom, which can be thought of as a natural clock the rhythm of which is revealed by its spectral line. Ives' subtle experiment showed not only that a moving hydrogen atom changes its rhythm but, what is much more important, that the change is exactly that predicted by relativity theory.

As we have seen, the revolution begun by relativity theory affects our traditional concepts of time and mass. Another concept that changed radically is that of length. Again we shall confine ourselves to describing the deduced result.

Let us return to our Fifth Avenue bus. As we said before, this bus is four blocks long while standing still. But how long is it when it moves? We must distrust our prejudices and beware of asserting what seems obvious at first. Instead of replying, "Of course, it is always four blocks long," as the classical physicist would have said, let us be more cautious. Let us ask instead, "What do you mean when you inquire how long it is when it moves?" I would suggest the following answer: You know that the bus moves with a speed, say, half that of light. Then you stand with a stop-watch and press it when the front of the bus passes you. You press it again when the rear of the bus passes you. In this way you will arrive at how long it takes for the bus to pass you. Multiply this small period by the speed of the bus and you will have its length while in motion. You can conceive of other arrangements, but you will not find any reasonable experiment which does not involve the use of a clock. But time is relative and clocks, as we have seen, change their rhythms while in motion. Thus, it would not be astonishing if the result of such an experiment should show that length is relative, too. Indeed, in our case, in which the bus travels with the velocity of half that of light, its length would be shortened by about fifteen per cent. Its dimensions would shrink to nothing in the direction of the motion if the speed were that of light. Length, like time, is relative.

I have tried to sketch here the revolutionary changes effected by Einstein's two papers. What was the impact of these new ideas? At first there was hardly any. Nowadays important results are perhaps more quickly recognized and a revolutionary new paper often produces a flood of other contributions, written by men who build up the ideas in greater detail and who develop them mathematically. But such a flood of papers did not occur immediately after the appearance of Einstein's articles. It began some four years later—a long time interval for scientific recognition. Yet I know that there were physicists who read Einstein's paper very carefully in the interim and who saw in it the birth of a new science. My friend Professor Loria told me how his teacher, Professor Witkowski in Cracow (and a very great teacher he was!), read Einstein's paper and exclaimed to Loria, "A new Copernicus has been born! Read Einstein's paper." Later, when Professor Loria met Professor Max Born at a physics meeting, he told him about Einstein and asked Born if he had read the paper. It turned out that neither Born nor anyone else there had heard about Einstein. They went to the library, took from the bookshelves the seventeenth volume of *Annalen der Physik* and started to read Einstein's article. Immediately Max Born recognized its greatness and also the necessity for formal generalizations. Later, Born's own work on relativity theory became one of the most important early contributions to this field of science.

But it was not before 1908 or 1909 that the attention of great numbers of scientists was drawn to Einstein's results. One of the contributing factors in making relativity more widely familiar was the appearance of Minkowski's lecture, "Space and Time," in 1908. Herman Minkowski was a great mathematician who was then professor at Göttingen. The famous lecture that he gave at the eightieth meeting of the Association of Scientists and Doctors (*Naturforscher und Ärzte*) was, I believe, his last public lecture, for he died prematurely very soon after. The first words of Minkowski's lecture were a prophetic statement of the profound influence which Einstein's ideas would exert on modern thought:

> Gentlemen! The views of time and space that I wish to develop before you grew on the soil of physical experiments. There lies their strength. Their tendency is radical. From now on, space in itself and time in itself should descend into a shadow and only a union of both should retain its independence.

Minkowski's mathematical genius put Einstein's ideas into a new geometrical form that fully revealed their beauty and simplicity. Sometimes we hear that "time is a fourth dimension in relativity theory," and we are impressed by the mystical sound of these words. But there is nothing mystical about them. Events in the world must be described by four numbers, three of them referring to positions and one to time. Minkowski showed that it is much more convenient not to treat space alone as the background of our events, but space-time. The splitting of such a space-time background into space and time depends on the *system* of observation. We cannot say more here about Minkowski's mathematical work on relativity theory because it is not possible to describe a mathematical formalism without the use of mathematical symbols.

Between 1908 and 1918, relativity theory became known to physicists and mathematicians. Many of them became aware that a revolution had taken place. But the enthusiasm and doubts were subdued. Only later were both reactions voiced more loudly than ever before in the history of science.

CHAPTER FOUR

THE SECOND EINSTEIN REVOLUTION

THE FALLING ELEVATOR

THE first Einstein revolution was accomplished. Perhaps the man least satisfied with the results achieved was Einstein himself. Soon he saw that the revolution had not gone far enough, that deep difficulties were still present in physics.

Many years later in Princeton I said to Einstein, "I believe that special relativity theory would have been formulated with but little delay whether or not you had done it. The times were ripe for it." Einstein answered, "Yes, this is true, but not of general relativity theory. I doubt if it would be known yet." I believe that this answer well characterizes Einstein's role in the second revolution.

Anticipating what happened, let us introduce two terms that are used today in discussing relativity: *special* (or restricted) and *general*. We shall use the term *special* relativity theory when referring to the ideas we have described in the preceding chapter and *general* relativity when speaking about the later development, which we shall now take up.

Special relativity theory was in the air. The contradictions that it removed were known to physicists, for the sores on the body of physics were visible to many; but that was not the case with general relativity theory. Einstein was the only man who still saw contradictions and difficulties, and who worked for their removal. In the case of special relativity theory the sickness was known; only the healing formula was unknown. General relativity theory was more like the remedy for a serious illness of which no one was aware but Einstein and, to a certain extent, a Viennese philosopher, Ernst Mach. Even Planck, the great Planck, who began the development of quantum theory, said to Einstein, "Everything now is so nearly settled, why do you bother about these other problems?" Yet bother Einstein did, and by himself. Eight years divide special and general relativity theory; eight years of constant thought that finally bore fruit in the new solution of the great problem of gravitation.

I have before me a paper that Einstein wrote in 1911 while a professor in Prague. It appeared in *Annalen der Physik* under the title "The Influence of Gravitation upon the Propagation of Light." It is a most interesting paper because, more than any other, it reveals the path of Einstein's thoughts. In part it is wrong: it contains half-truths, conjecture, a dramatic awareness that the real truth is not far off yet very different. It shows the first glimmer of light breaking through darkness. It also reflects Einstein's passion for idealized experiments and his childlike ability to wonder about simple things; so simple and familiar, indeed, that they are as unnoticed by others as the postman in one of the Father Brown stories.

Since Galileo, physicists have known that all bodies fall with the same acceleration. All bodies allowed to fall from the same height will reach the ground after the same time interval, if we may neglect air resistance. Galileo showed how one could deduce this law from simple idealized experiments and how experiments of the kind made with falling stones or pendulums confirm such a law. No one in our century, with the exception of Einstein, wondered about this law any longer. Experiment had shown that, so far as we can determine, the law is rigorously valid. There is not the slightest difference between the accelerations of various bodies falling at the same place on our earth.

Education kills our ability to wonder. Only genius can remain unspoiled. In the last three hundred years of the development of science, Einstein was the first who saw in this equality of accelerations an important missing clue. We can imagine a world in which such a law is not valid; a world in which elephants fall so slowly that they almost float through the air while babies fall with a dangerously great acceleration toward the earth. But the gravitational field of our earth forces babies and elephants to fall with the same acceleration. What is the significance of this important clue? In the framework of classical mechanics it appears as a mere accident!

Einstein told me how, since his boyhood, he thought about the man running after the light ray and the man closed in a falling elevator. The picture of the man running after the light ray led to special relativity theory. The picture of the man in a falling elevator led to general relativity theory. In Einstein's paper which I have just quoted we find implicitly the picture of a man in a falling elevator. We must discuss this picture.

Let us imagine a skyscraper. An elevator is raised to its heights and then released so that it falls *freely* with a uniformly accelerated motion. The observers inside it are not afraid of the coming collision with the bottom of the shaft but are bravely pursuing their investigations. To perfect our picture, let us imagine that the elevator is made of glass, so that observers from the outside can look in, and that the observers in the elevator and observers on the ground are able to compare notes with each other. There is a similarity between the technique of reasoning that we have used before and the technique we shall use now. Again we have two *systems*—the elevator and the earth—but there is also a crucial difference. The relative motion of the two *systems* is no longer *uniform* but is now *accelerated*. Yet our technique of explanation will remain similar. Again we shall ask questions of the observers inside and outside the elevator and again simple reasoning will lead us to far-reaching conclusions.

The operator in the elevator uses her compact and lipstick and then lets go of both. We ask: what happens to the lipstick and the compact? This is not a trivial question. The answer is: when judged from inside the elevator the lipstick and the compact remain at rest where she released them. Why shouldn't they? All objects fall with the same acceleration relative to the earth. Thus, relative to each other they are at rest. Objects dropped in the freely falling elevator do not fall to its floor or rise to the ceiling. They stay where they were when they were released. What happens if the operator pushes the compact? The compact will then move with *uniform motion* in the direction in which it was pushed, until a collision with the wall of the elevator stops it. After some experiments the observer inside the elevator will formulate the following law: all bodies in my *system* either remain at rest or move uniformly until disturbed by forces, or by the walls of my *system*, or by the coming end of our world—that is, the coming crash of the elevator with the bottom of the shaft. This is *almost* the Newtonian law of inertia that we learned in school. I say *"almost,"* because in schools we talked about neither the restriction of walls, nor the end of the world.

We must pause here to emphasize the importance of our picture.

According to Newton's law of inertia (the first of Newton's three celebrated laws), all bodies are either at rest or in uniform motion until disturbed by the action of external forces. Is this law true? If you drop a body on the earth it will not remain at rest; it will fall down. No mother will try to check the law of inertia by dropping her baby from the window. Newtonian mechanics tells us that the law of inertia is not valid because there is a force in our *system*: the force of gravitation. To avoid the effects of this gravitational force, you may push some spheres on a horizontal plane, say, on a smooth table. Again, after some time, these spheres will cease to move. Then the Newtonian mechanist will explain to you that they did not move uniformly because there was friction; to test the law of inertia you must remove the friction too. But it is even worse than that. Imagine that you perform your experiments on a merry-go-round. There, every particle is thrown out, away from the center of the merry-go-round. Thus, the Newtonian laws of mechanics are not valid on a merry-go-round, for there an observer will find that a particle does not remain at rest but tries to move as far from the center as possible. But if the law of inertia is not valid on the merry-go-round, then it is not valid on our earth, which also rotates.

I think we are justified in being perplexed by all this and in asking the Newtonian mechanist a simple question:

"Where, for Heaven's sake, *is* your *system* in which the law of inertia is valid?"

If he is honest, he will tell you:

"I don't know. You must look for it. The earth is sometimes a good approximation to such a *system* and sometimes it is not. It depends on your problem and on the degree of accuracy of your experiments. All I know is that if you find one such *system,* then you have an infinity of them because any other *system* moving uniformly relative to the one good *system* is a good *system* too."

Our discussion has brought out a disastrously weak point in the doctrine of classical mechanics. We know the laws but we do not know the *system* to which they refer. Since the usual way out of a difficulty is to invent a new name, we call a *system* in which the laws of mechanics are valid an *inertial system*; but we cannot say "this or that is an inertial *system*." We know only theoretically what an inertial *system* is. It is one in which the law of mechanics are valid. But we don't know whether or where such *systems* exist.

There was a time when to criticize Newton was in bad taste—almost a crime. Even in the second half of the nineteenth century it required great independence of mind to look critically at Newton's structure, magnificent but not unsurpassed. The man who did this for the first time was the Viennese philosopher, Ernst Mach. Einstein was influenced by Mach, although his own criticism is incomparably sharper. The irony is that when Einstein removed these difficulties from physics, Mach was then too old to understand the importance of Einstein's work.

We return to our observers in the falling elevator. As Einstein pointed out, we have here a model of an *almost inertial system.* It is inertial, but not quite. Its inertial character is restricted in space. The *system* is not fully inertial because sooner or later the operator's lipstick, if pushed, will collide with the wall. To make the elevator bigger and bigger is not a remedy, because we know that all bodies fall with the same acceleration only if they are at the same point in space or in the immediate neighborhood of a point. Thus our elevator must not be too big. Then our inertial *system* is, of course, restricted in time, for the world of our inside observer will come to an end through the inevitable catastrophe of collision. We call such a *system,* as represented by the elevator, an *almost inertial system.* Thus we may say that Einstein's idealized experiment indicated the existence of an almost inertial *system.*

Up to now we have talked only about observers inside the elevator. The observer outside has very little to say that is new or interesting. Obviously his *system* is not inertial, because of the force of gravity. For him, the elevator, the operator, her lipstick, compact, all fall with the same acceleration in the gravitational field of the earth.

We detect in Einstein's reasoning the familiar pattern: important conclusions drawn from simple idealized experiments. We shall follow some of them.

We have two *systems* (the elevator and the earth with the elevator shaft) in relative accelerated motion. One *system,* the elevator, is almost inertial. In such a *system,* the laws of mechanics are almost rigorously valid; there is no gravitation there, because it has been wiped out by the free motion of the elevator. (But the observer outside will say that his *system* is not inertial because of the gravitational field in which all bodies fall with the same acceleration.) Looking through the transparent floor of their elevator, the inhabitants will see that a huge body rushes toward them. Knowing nothing about gravitational forces, and assuming the validity of Newtonian mechanics, they will see the accelerated motion of this body and with horror they will say that some constant force pushes it in their direction in order to destroy their world. Thus, these observers, in a limited space and in a limited time, can describe their observations consistently, using Newtonian mechanics and without assuming a gravitational field.

Before, when discussing special relativity theory, we saw

that a consistent description of events in two *systems* is possible if these two *systems* are in uniform relative motion. The transition from one *system* to another is governed by the Lorentz transformation. But now we have two *systems* moving with accelerated motion relative to each other. Any transition from one *system* to another now involves the appearance of a gravitational field in one of them and its disappearance in the other. Thus, if we wish to enlarge our considerations by including *systems* whose relative motion is not uniform, we must take into account the all-important phenomenon of gravitation. It is the link connecting *systems* in non-uniform motion. The gravitational field can be wiped out or created (at least locally) by the choice of a proper reference system! This is true only because in a gravitational field all bodies have the same acceleration at a given point. Without this simple clue, ignored for three hundred years, all that has been said here would be meaningless and general relativity theory, as we know it, impossible. Our simple considerations show us that this forgotten clue is not accidental but fundamental, when properly understood. Indeed, it leads us to general relativity theory.

Our argument was simple, and no mathematics was necessary. But even these qualitative arguments will lead us to a new conclusion that can either be confirmed or rejected by experiment.

Earlier, while discussing special relativity theory, we drew a most important conclusion; we found the connection between mass and energy. To use a cliché, this result led to the greatest discovery since the discovery of fire. Now, starting from our example of the falling elevator, we shall deduce a conclusion that played a most important role in making people all over the world conscious of relativity theory and its creator.

Let us imagine two small holes drilled in the opposite walls of our elevator at exactly the same height. Into one of these holes we push a flashlight and, by turning it on and off, we send light signals to the opposite wall of this elevator. Obviously, because the freely falling elevator is an almost inertial *system*, the light in it will travel along a straight line, with constant speed, and after a very short time interval, will meet the hole drilled in the opposite wall. This argument is convincing. All we have done is to apply the laws of propagation of light, assumed to be valid in an inertial *system*. But what about the observer outside, on the earth, for whom a gravitational field exists? Through the glass walls he will see the light signal coming from one wall and reaching the opposite wall. But during the short time interval (and let us imagine everything as in a slow-motion film) while the light signal moves toward the second wall the entire elevator moves down for the observer outside. This is true even if the elevator starts its downward journey just at the moment the light signal is sent. Even if the initial velocity of the elevator is zero, its acceleration is not zero and the elevator will move down slightly while the light ray completes its journey to the opposite wall. The light will appear leaving the elevator at a lower level than that of its entrance.

What will this outside observer say? Obviously he will say that the light ray is curved in a gravitational field, that the gravitational field deforms the straight path of a light ray. As a matter of fact, if the observer knows special relativity theory, he should be neither shocked nor astonished. He knows from special relativity theory that every energy has mass and every mass has energy. The moving light ray carries energy with it and therefore it is natural that it should be deflected in the gravitational field just as the path of a projectile thrown horizontally is curved in a gravitational field. This effect will be very small, but a light ray sent from a star and passing the edge of the sun should be deflected in a way that could perhaps be detected by observation. During a solar eclipse we can photograph stars in the neighborhood of the darkened sun. This means that the light rays sent from these stars pass near the edge of the sun on their journey toward our earth. Let us compare such a photograph with a photograph of the same fragment of the heavens when the sun is in a different position. Two such pictures must be slightly different because in one case the light rays were deflected by the gravitational field of the sun and not deflected in the other. In his paper of 1911, Einstein calculated the deflection and predicted the phenomenon of bending of light under the influence of a gravitational field. This calculation was not exactly correct. The numerical result that Einstein quoted was too small. He still did not have the full knowledge of general relativity theory. He was to gain it during the next four years, when he was to return to his calculations and revise them. But the prediction of this effect already appeared in Einstein's paper of 1911. He finished it with these notable words:

> It would be urgently desirable for astronomers to become interested in this question, even if the considerations given here appear insufficiently founded or even adventurous. Regardless of any theory, one must ask oneself whether with our present means we can find an influence of the gravitational field upon the propagation of light.

What became of Einstein's challenge to astronomers? Eight years passed. In the meantime Einstein moved from Prague to Zürich, then from Zürich to Berlin. There the first world war caught him and there he finished his work on general relativity theory.

The appreciation of relativity theory spread slowly, from theoretical physicists to experimental physicists, astronomers, mathematicians, and philosophers. It was considered an extremely difficult subject requiring the knowledge of methods in mathematics which at that time were neither generally known nor sufficiently developed. Indeed Riemannian geometry and later the so-called non-Riemannian geometry were developed fully because of the need of physicists for suitable mathematical tools. Relativity theory greatly stimulated the growth of this branch of mathematics, nowadays taught at every great university, often even as an undergraduate course.

Only after the war did the knowledge of general relativity theory spread to England and other Allied countries. In 1919 two English expeditions were sent out, one to Sobral in Brazil, the other to Principe on the coast of Africa. When the moon eclipsed the sun and night interrupted daylight, the scientists photographed the stars visible in the sun's neighborhood. Then for months they performed tedious measurements and calculations to find whether light rays bend in a gravitational field and whether this effect agrees quantitatively with that foreseen by general relativity theory. When announced at the time, the results seemed splendidly to confirm Einstein's prediction. (Later measurements spoiled this agreement slightly. But there is little doubt today that light rays are deflected by the gravitational field.)

No one knows why, but suddenly this phenomenon of bending light rays captured the imagination of the entire civilized world. Was the reason for it the romantic scenery? Or was it the desire to escape into abstract thoughts and to forget the bitter taste of victory and defeat? Or was it the belief that this confirmation of the work of a German scientist by English scientists was the beginning of a new era in which men would forgive, forget, and work together? I am well aware how difficult it is to answer these questions. The fact remains that suddenly, soon after 1920, the whole world became aware of relativity theory and its creator. A lonely man who never sought publicity became the most famous man in the world, the most praised and the most ridiculed. He was as indifferent to both as to many other details of external life. Perhaps he was less aware of this sudden fame than anyone else.

THREE THEMES

We have sketched the beginning of general relativity theory as it appeared in Einstein's work of 1911. The next few years led to its finished structure, based on new ideas. We can still grasp them even if we are not able to follow their mathematical formulation. They are connected with the following three themes:

First: Gravitation
Second: Invariance
Third: The relation between geometry and physics

We shall discuss them in turn.

Perhaps the greatest triumph of Newtonian mechanics was

its solution of the problem of gravitation. A silly legend states that Newton saw an apple falling from the tree and, though the apple did not strike his head, suddenly the idea of gravitational forces did. A story of this kind is far from the true situation. Newton found the theory of gravitation because he had thought about it consciously and unconsciously for years and years. A scientist may suddenly see the light, or rather the first glimmer of light, but only after long and incessant thought.

In the nineteenth century, the development of astronomy culminated in Laplace's great work, *Mécanique céleste,* based on the Newtonian law of gravitation. Yet, as time went on, this Newtonian law seemed more and more unsatisfactory. According to Newton, the motion of the earth, moon, stars, planets, and sun are governed by the same law. The moon moves around the earth because the earth attracts the moon. The earth and other planets move around the sun because they are attracted by it, and this attraction diminishes as the distance increases, since it is inversely proportional to the square of the distance. This picture, of particles with gravitational forces acting between them, belongs to the Newtonian view and it is the culminating point of this view.

But, as we now know, the field view was at least as successful in the description of electromagnetic and light phenomena as the mechanical view was in astronomy. The field theory brought a new point of view into physics. For the modern physicist any action or force spreads from the source to the recipient with a finite speed: the speed of light in the case of the electromagnetic field. The force changes both in time and in space. It is artificial to imagine that gravitational action, on the other hand, does not depend on time; that if somewhere in the universe a new star were created the entire universe would feel its presence at the single moment of its creation. The field theory asserts that actions spread with finite speed and that the laws governing these changes in space and time are the laws of the field. Therefore, the Newtonian theory of gravitation, which does not formulate such field laws, appears, in contrast, unsatisfactory and artificial. Besides, it fits only into the framework of classical mechanics where time and space are absolute and where an inertial *system* is assumed to exist. But we know by now that time is not absolute. Even if time does not enter the picture in one inertial *system* it must enter the picture in another inertial *system,* according to the Lorentz transformation. The old Newtonian law fits the narrow framework of classical mechanics but does not fit the broader framework of special relativity theory. The Newtonian law of gravitation assumes, furthermore, the existence of an inertial *system,* although classical mechanics is unable to tell us how to find such a *system.* Confronted by a result which contradicts observation, a classical mechanist has two choices: he can say that Newton's laws are not valid or he can say that he has chosen a non-inertial *system.* Really, if he believes in classical mechanics, then the first explanation, that the Newtonian laws are invalid, is prohibited by his beliefs. But then the entire problem of confirming or rejecting Newtonian laws becomes meaningless.

The criticisms discussed here are due partially to Mach and partially to Einstein. We summarize them:

The Newtonian gravitational law assumes the existence of an inertial *system.*

The Newtonian gravitational law does not fit the frame of special relativity theory.

The Newtonian gravitational law is not the law of a gravitational field changing in time and space.

In the Newtonian gravitational law the equality of accelerations at a given point in space appears as an accident to which no deeper meaning can be attached.

Each of these objections is a grave one and there are four of them!

General relativity theory attacked the problem of gravitation in an entirely new way and in one bold stroke removed all these difficulties. How this is done is a different question and not easy to answer. Yet, we shall try to explain some of the new and revolutionary ideas on which Einstein based his general relativity theory.

Special relativity theory enlarges the framework of classical physics. General relativity theory in turn enlarges the framework of special relativity theory; it must be used if, and when, gravitational forces cannot be ignored. We can derive special relativity theory from the higher view of general relativity theory if gravitational forces can be ignored. Inside the falling elevator we have a *system* which, to some extent, is almost the inertial *system* of special relativity theory. But while making measurements in large areas, over long time intervals, we cannot assume the validity of special relativity theory inside a giant falling elevator.

Thus we climb higher and higher to free ourselves of more and more restrictions. The road becomes more and more difficult, but at each step forward we must be able to retain the advantages of our old view.

If we wish to find a new theory of gravitation free from the shortcomings of the old one, we must remember, and this is important, the tremendous wealth of experiences satisfactorily explained by the old theory. The new theory, logically more consistent and simple, must explain the known facts just as well. The earth moves in an ellipse around the sun. This follows from the Newtonian law of motion and Newton's theory of gravitation. It follows, too, from Einstein's theory of gravitation. But we do expect some small disagreements between the old and new theories. They must be small, for otherwise they would have been detected a long time ago. But whenever they lie beyond experimental error they must be confirmed by observation. One such conclusion, new and unknown to classical mechanics, was the deflection of light in a gravitational field.

One often overemphasizes the importance of experimental evidence in the case of general relativity theory. Truly speaking, the evidence is still pretty thin though there is little doubt that general relativity theory fits known facts better than Newtonian mechanics. But it is not here that the strength of general relativity theory lies, but rather in its inner consistency, in the removal of the old difficulties and in its greater logical simplicity.

If we remember the role of astronomy and the Newtonian

law of gravitation in the history of our civilization, we shall understand the importance of the Einstein revolution which, for the first time in the history of science, revised the problem of gravitation. But perhaps more important than that is the revolution this theory has accomplished in our physical and philosophical thinking.

We have said that Einstein's theory of gravitation is logically simpler than the Newtonian theory. This requires clarification, for ordinarily general relativity theory is regarded as very difficult compared with the Newtonian theory. Even if we appreciate that the statement about only twelve people comprehending relativity theory is ridiculous, there is no denying that technically general relativity theory is much more difficult to grasp than classical mechanics. True enough, this statement is most often made by those who understand neither. It is not at all easy to deduce from the Newtonian theory of gravitation that the earth travels along an ellipse around the sun. Besides a knowledge of Newtonian mechanics, such a deduction requires some knowledge of calculus and differential equations. To deduce the same result in general relativity theory is more difficult yet. It requires knowledge and understanding of the mathematical structure of relativity theory, and this, in turn, demands knowledge of Riemannian geometry and tensor calculus, the branches of mathematics that developed under the influence of relativity theory. The deduction in itself is much longer, much more tedious and, in the case of our earth we find complicated equations of motion which in the first approximation give us the old equations of Newton. However, we can still maintain that Einstein's theory is logically simpler than the old Newtonian theory if we distinguish between *logical* and *technical* simplicity. By removing artificial and unnecessary assumptions, we achieve greater logical simplicity. But then our deductions are longer and more tedious. We have assumed less and must therefore deduce more. It sounds paradoxical, but general relativity theory appears to be difficult just because it is so simple and assumes so little.

If two bodies, *A* and *B*—say, the earth and the sun—are in relative motion, then it is, of course, meaningless to assume that *A* rests and *B* moves or that *A* moves and *B* rests. All that we can observe is the motion of one body relative to the other. For example, to discuss the motion of one body in the entire universe is utterly meaningless, because motion means change in relative position. Today all this sounds like good common sense and it is regrettable that classical mechanics ever departed from this approach.

Ptolemy's theory, defended for a long time by the Church, claimed that the earth rests and the sun moves. Copernicus claimed, on the other hand, that the earth moves and the sun rests. But from the ordinary common-sense approach both these statements seem meaningless. Even if we agree that the sun stood still at Joshua's command, then obviously such a command implied that the sun stay still relative to the earth. Such a command is entirely equivalent to ordering the earth to stay still relative to the sun. I wonder whether such an argument would convince those who burned Giordano Bruno and put Galileo in prison. I rather doubt it, because Galileo's defense was almost exactly this. He claimed that hypothetically he considered a *system* in which the sun rests. But then again one can doubt whether Galileo was in a position to be sincere when confronted by the princes of the Church.

What, then, was all the fuss about? The answer is that classical mechanics departs from the "common-sense approach" by which we mean that there is only relative motion. According to classical mechanics there is one *system,* or rather a group of uniformly moving *systems,* in which the laws of physics are valid. It is this *system* (or rather these *systems*) to which we must refer motion and in which we can apply the laws of classical mechanics in all their beauty and simplicity. Thus, according to classical mechanics, we are able to speak about the motion of one body even if it is the only body in our universe. Imagine the room you are in, with its windows shut against the outside world. If a new force were to push all the objects in your room away from the center, you would deduce from classical mechanics that your *system* had ceased to be inertial because your room had begun to rotate.

Thus classical mechanics shatters our common-sense approach. We can detect motion even of one body; that is, we can detect *absolute* motion if the laws of mechanics, as formulated for an inertial *system,* are not valid in the *system* connected with this body.

This deviation of classical mechanics from the common-sense approach was criticized by Mach. We see how it is connected with the concept of an inertial *system.* Relativity theory returns to the common-sense approach. It formulates a principle which should be valid not only for gravitational phenomena but for *all* phenomena of nature. It is the principle of *invariance*:

The laws of nature must be valid in any system.

Whereas in special relativity theory we discuss *systems* moving uniformly relative to each other, in general relativity theory we discuss *systems* in arbitrary relative motion. There is no absolute motion. The statement that the earth moves or the sun moves is meaningless. We have new laws that we can apply either to a *system* connected with the sun or to a *system* connected with the earth. It may be more convenient for some special problems to connect our *system* with the sun, but the difference is only of a technical nature. Logically, both *systems* are equivalent and any *system* is allowable.

It may seem that general relativity theory tackled two different problems, that of gravitation and that of formulating laws of nature for an arbitrary *system.* But these two problems are fundamentally one. You remember the important example of the falling elevator, where we considered two *systems* moving non-uniformly relative to each other. One was almost inertial and in the other we had a gravitational field. It is this gravitational field that appears or disappears in small regions if we pass from one *system* to another (if we wish to exclude gravitation then we must restrict the *systems* to those moving uniformly). It is the gravitational field that allows us to formulate laws valid for any *system.* The gravitational field can be, I repeat, created or annihilated in small regions by the process of transformation.

Thus the discussion of the falling elevator gives us the right clue. The end result of a long chain of arguments leading from this clue is:

1. The formulation of field laws of the gravitational field. Like Maxwell's equations for the electromagnetic field, Einstein's field equations describe changes of the gravitational field in space and time. These equations in all their generality and beauty were formulated by Einstein. They look simple, yet they are the most difficult equations to work with. But if the gravitational field is weak we can show comparatively easily that in the first approximation these equations reduce to the old Newtonian equations. I am tempted to write down Einstein's field equations for empty space, and I can do it in part of a line. They are: $R_{kl} = 0$; but to know what R_{kl} means and what is the structure of these equations you must have the proper technical knowledge. It can be gained after, say, two or three years of study by almost anyone who likes mathematics (usually those who like mathematics have sufficient ability to understand it). But once we understand these equations we know the most essential part of general relativity theory.

2. General relativity theory makes it possible to formulate laws of nature for an arbitrary *system*. Thus, the disturbing ghost of the inertial *system* is gone from physics, and we are free to choose any *system* we wish. Our laws are valid in each and every one of them. In more technical language we say: the laws of physics are *invariant* with respect to an arbitrary transformation.

We see how deeply general relativity theory changes our physical concepts. Indeed it is a revolution comparable only with that accomplished by Newton or Maxwell. It also clarifies the connection between *physics* and *geometry*, changing our views about this old philosophical problem.

The classical physicist assumed that our three-dimensional space was Euclidean and that time was absolute. In special relativity theory we consider space and time as a four-dimensional background of our events. According to general relativity theory, such a background is of a non-Euclidean character. To solve the problem of gravitation in accordance with our field views, and to introduce laws valid in any *system,* we are forced to consider the time-space geometry in a new way. It is here that the connection between geometry and physics comes in.

This part of the structure, the mathematical part, took most of the time and effort in Einstein's work. Einstein has never considered himself a mathematician. He rightly regards himself as a philosopher because the physical problems that he tackled are closely related to philosophical problems that have bothered thinking men throughout the history of our civilization. But these problems, like those of time, space, geometry, were shifted by Einstein from the field of speculation into the field of physics, into the field of science, of rigorous reasoning, whose tool is mathematics. Einstein learned mathematics when he needed it and for the purpose for which he needed it. Learned? It would be better to say that he reinvented it, always preferring to think for himself than to read books. In the case of general relativity theory, the mathematical apparatus that he needed at first was still crude, only in its infancy. Later it grew quickly because of the expanding needs of general relativity theory.

While I was in Berlin, Einstein gave a lecture to the Prussian Academy of Science about the connection between geometry and experience. Later he repeated the lecture for the university students. I was one of the listeners, and no one who studied relativity theory could fail to be impressed by the depth and simplicity of Einstein's philosophical ideas and the charm with which he explained them. Then there was the question period and many muddle-headed philosophers asked muddled questions. "What about Kant?" "What you said, Herr Professor, contradicts Kant." Indeed! How can one contradict Kant, and in Berlin, too! Einstein, as always, enjoyed the spectacle. He was neither angry nor impatient when he heard the words "transcendental," " a priori," "Weltanschauung," and all the rubbish that relativity theory swept away and which still today haunts volumes of books and many departments of speculative philosophy. Empty words die hard!

What, then, is the connection between geometry and physics? To understand this, let us simplify our problem.

We imagine thinking creatures living on a two-dimensional plane. We can watch their action and even be moved by it, as anyone knows who has shed tears in a movie. But we must not take the movie comparison too seriously. We imagine the screen infinitely great, forget perspective, and visualize flat creatures with only one profile, like those on an Egyptian painting. We assume, too, that these creatures have brains and act of their own accord. For them the two-dimensional plane will be what three-dimensional space is for us. If they are intelligent, they may, in time, develop the knowledge of plane Euclidean geometry; that is, the same geometry that we know from our high school days. Once they start a journey along a straight line they will never return to the point of their departure; two parallel lines will never meet and the circumference of a circle will be 2π times the radius of this circle. These creatures—we may imagine—may even have a primitive kind of physics. They may have experimented with light rays; they may have developed the concepts of time and velocity; they may have found that the speed of light—as in our three-dimensional space—is 186,000 miles per second.

Having begun our story of the two-dimensional creatures, let us proceed to its second chapter. We imagine that at some moment when all these creatures were asleep someone transplanted them onto the surface of a sphere, let us say; a very big sphere. What do we mean by saying that a sphere is very big? We mean that these creatures will not detect any difference when they wake up. Their communications are not sufficiently developed to discover that once they start a journey "straight ahead" they will ultimately return to the point of their departure. When drawing a small circle, they will not find that its circumference is slightly smaller than 2π times the radius of the circle. But as generations of two-dimensional creatures die and are born, and as their science and technique become more and more perfected, they will find out that something is wrong with their heritage of Euclidean geometry. They will conclude that it is more convenient and more consistent with their observations to use, not the Euclidean geometry of a plane, but the non-Euclidean geometry of a sphere! For some time the more conservative elements of their community will resist such an innovation and perhaps burn in a two-dimensional fire the creatures preaching non-Euclidean geometry. These conservative creatures may say that the rods used were not perfectly rigid, that there were some differences in temperature accounting for the apparent breakdown of Euclidean geometry. But finally science will, as it always does, win in such a struggle. Slowly the two-dimensional inhabitants of the sphere will recognize that it is much more convenient to assume non-Euclidean spherical geometry. Thus, they will learn that a "straight line" (a great circle to you) is always closed, that a light ray sent from any point *P* returns to its point of departure. They will pronounce the last results even if they cannot travel all around the sphere, even if a hundred generations must be born, die, and be born before they find by an actual experiment that a light ray does return to its point of departure. They will deduce these results because now in their neighborhood the geometry of a non-Euclidean character describes phenomena better and more economically than the old Euclidean geometry. A scientific revolution will have taken place among these two-dimensional creatures!

This story is not as fantastic as it sounds. Indeed, some of its features remind us of the story of our earth and how its spherical shape was recognized.

We return to the two-dimensional creatures to tell the third and last chapter of our tale. Imagine that a new change has taken place. Again something has happened suddenly to these creatures while they were asleep. This time the event was not in the realm of geometry but rather of physics. (If there is any sense in a clear-cut distinction between geometry and physics.) You can picture the creatures living on the sphere, and single out two opposite points on this sphere which we shall call the North and the South Pole. The temperature of the sphere, which has been—let us say—uniform, undergoes a sudden change. It is cold at the poles, warmer away from them, and the equator is the hottest line. It is so cold at the poles that the temperature there is absolute zero. This means that the dimensions of all the living creatures, of all the rigid rods, so *we assume,* shrink to zero as they approach these poles. Thus the creatures travelling toward the poles become smaller and smaller, their dimensions, their steps, smaller and smaller, and they will never reach the poles. Travelling along the circles of latitude, they may find, if the temperatures are properly adjusted, that every such circle is just as long as the equator, because their rods and their own dimensions have shrunk so as to account exactly for this very fact; the circles become smaller but so do their measuring rods.

Thus, our intelligent two-dimensional creatures are faced with an entirely new situation and they have two ways of adjusting their science to their changed world. If their two-dimensional bodies are not sensitive to the change in temperature, then they may assume that they live now, not on a plane, not on a sphere, but on an infinite cylinder. It will be infinite for them because they can never reach the end while going north or south. But it will be finite if they travel along parallel circles, and all these circles will have the same radii because they know nothing of the change of scale that we noticed when looking at their sphere with the advantages of three-dimensional human beings.

On the other hand, if they are susceptible to cold and heat, they may prefer to assume that they still live on a sphere and that on this sphere there are now two very singular points which they will never reach because the temperature there is absolute zero.

No one knows what will be the choice of these creatures. It depends on many circumstances which we do not wish to analyze. They may even have two rival theories.

Our story has a deep moral. It shows how intimately physics is connected with geometry. Remember that the two-dimensional creatures have a choice between assuming differences in temperature and spherical geometry on the one hand, or, on the other hand, no differences in temperature and the geometry of a cylinder (which is essentially a Euclidean geometry).

We three-dimensional creatures are in a similar situation. We must treat geometry and physics as *one* system of knowledge. Our scientific task is to formulate such a single system, most consistent and convenient for the description of the phenomena of nature. The system is good if it works.

Relativity theory taught us that if we wish to abandon the empty concepts of an inertial *system,* if we wish to formulate field laws for gravitation, if we wish to formulate invariant laws that are valid in any system, if we wish to do all this, then we must assume a non-Euclidean geometry of our four-dimensional time-space. It is the gravitational field that characterizes the geometry of our world. A rubber plane can be deformed by the stresses of external forces. Similarly, moving masses deform our space-time. They determine whether, and to what degree, our time-space is non-Euclidean. The two questions, "What is the geometry of our world?" and "What is the gravitational field of our world?" are identical questions. Geometry and gravitation become synonymous. They are determined by the distribution of masses and their speeds. I have quoted before the equations of general relativity theory for empty space. These are the equations that describe both the geometry and the gravitational field of our world in regions from which matter is absent.

I am well aware that these ideas are difficult. In some respects, to understand relativity theory using mathematics is simpler than to understand it without mathematics. Yet, I hope I have shown how basic the new concepts are, how deep are the philosophical implications of relativity and how radically this theory changed the science of our world.

Among conclusions that can be drawn from general relativity theory that are different from those of classical mechanics, there is one that is well known: the perihelion motion of Mercury. In 1916 it formed the first confirmation of relativity theory. This conclusion was rigorously deduced at that time from Einstein's equations by a famous astronomer, Schwarzschild.

Yet, in some respects this statement is an oversimplification, and the full history of this problem is much more complicated. I shall report on it briefly.

The structure of general relativity theory progressed comparatively slowly, formulated and reformulated in papers published by Einstein in the proceedings of the Prussian Academy. More than once Einstein had to retrace his steps, correct mistakes, as he penetrated deeper and deeper into the problem of gravitation. Around 1916 the structure of general relativity theory was finished and once more summarized in a long paper that appeared in *Annalen der Physik* under the title "The Foundations of General Relativity Theory." No essential changes were made later, though many results were added and developed.

General relativity theory, as formulated around 1916, rested on two pillars. One of them represented the equations of the *field*; that is, the equations describing the change in space and time of the gravitational or, if you prefer, the geometrical field. The other represented the equations of *motion,* telling us how a particle moves in such a gravitational field. These equations replaced the old Newtonian equations of motion in which the gravitational force is proportional to acceleration. But now, in general relativity theory, the equations of motion, like all laws of nature, are valid not only in an inertial but in an arbitrary *system*.

Thus, if we wish to find, say, the motion of a planet in the gravitational field of the sun, we have first to find the gravitational field of the sun from the field equations of general relativity theory. Later we must apply the equations of motion in this known field and find the motion of a planet. This is precisely what Schwarzschild did with great mathematical skill. But his result is valid only if the planet is small compared with the sun. Astronomers know about the existence of many double stars—two bodies moving around each other like two suns. We cannot assume that one is small compared with the other. We cannot treat such a motion of double stars by the method of Schwarzschild because, as far as the equation of motion in general relativity theory is concerned, all we know is that this equation can be applied only to a small body (a planet) in a field which is not too much disturbed by the presence of such a small body.

We have field equations and equations of motion; but the equations of motion, as known explicitly in general relativity theory, have only a restricted validity. Until 1938 we did not know how to solve the problem of motion for double stars in general relativity theory, though we knew how to solve this problem in classical mechanics. There it is hardly more difficult than the problem of a heavy sun and a small planet.

For a long time Einstein believed that equations of motion are unnecessary in general relativity theory, that such equations do not need to be assumed, that they can be *deduced* from the field equations, that we can cross out and forget the equations of motion, that the *only* pillar on which general relativity rests is constructed of the field equations alone.

This proved to be true, but it took a long time to show it. All the technical means were in the hands of mathematicians and physicists about 1916. They knew the field equations. All that was needed was to show that these contained the equations of motion. It was like digging for a deeply buried treasure when we know the place where it is hidden. Einstein repeatedly tackled this problem, left it for many others, and again came back to it. Other scientists thought of it, too. In the meantime, Hitler came to power. Einstein left Germany and settled in Princeton in 1933 as a professor at the Institute for Advanced Study. This work on the problems of motion started about twenty-two years ago, but a logically satisfactory theory was given only recently (1949). It is this problem on which I collaborated with Einstein about twelve years ago and again during the present year.

Two morals can be drawn from this story. First, it shows how difficult the mathematical deductions are, how complicated are the equations of general relativity theory and how deeply they can hide their secrets. The second moral is of some philosophical significance and closely connected with the idea that we expressed before. It is logically simpler to assume only field equations and to disregard the equations of motion, but we have to pay for the logical simplicity by increased technical difficulties.

Now let us apply the equations of motion as deduced from the field equations (or as explicitly stated) to the motion of a small planet. Of course, in the first approximation we expect Newtonian motion because Newtonian theory follows from general relativity theory as its first approximation. But, if we go deeper, we find differences between Newtonian and general relativity theory, differences that can be confirmed by observation.

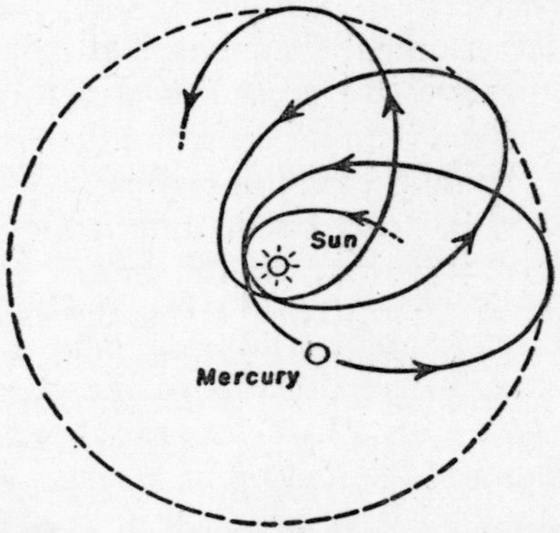

The ellipse that Mercury describes rotates very slowly relative to the *system* connected with the sun.

Such deviations from Newtonian laws can be expected only for strong gravitational fields. The planets, our earth among them, move along elliptical paths around the sun. Mercury is the planet nearest the sun, and the attraction between Mercury and the sun (using classical language) is therefore stronger than between the sun and any other planet. If there is hope of finding any deviation from Newton's law our best chance of doing so is in the case of Mercury. It follows from Newtonian theory that Mercury, like any other planet, moves along an ellipse, but this ellipse is the smallest, as compared with the paths of other planets in our solar system. But according to general relativity theory the motion should be slightly different. Not only should Mercury travel around the sun but the ellipse that it describes should rotate very slowly relative to the *system* connected with the sun. It is this rotation of the ellipse that expresses the new effect of general relativity theory and its deviation from the Newtonian theory. Relativity theory also predicts the magnitude of this effect: Mercury's ellipse should perform a complete rotation in three million years! We see how small this effect is and how much more difficult it would be to find a similar but still smaller effect for other planets.

The deviation of the motion of Mercury from the ellipse was known before general relativity theory was formulated, but no explanation could be found for it. On the other hand, Einstein developed the principles of general relativity theory without paying any attention to this special problem. His only aim was the removal of the logical inconsistencies and difficulties in the old theory. In the case of Mercury, general relativity theory explains successfully, not only qualitatively but also quantitatively, the deviation of its motion from the Newtonian laws.

Besides the two effects that we mentioned—that is, the deflection of light rays and the motion of Mercury—there is another effect, the so-called red-shift of spectral lines coming from the sun or from stars with a strong gravitational field. This effect, although easily deducible mathematically, is more difficult to explain than the others. Let us omit a more detailed account and just mention in passing that there, too, the verdict of experiment, though not very clear or decisive, seems to favor general relativity theory. But above all let us remember that the strength of this theory does not lie in such confirmations. Should there be no detectable differences between classical physics and general relativity theory we should still unreservedly choose general relativity theory. To deny this would mean not to understand the importance of the Einstein revolution and the great clarification, the logical and philosophical simplification that it brought to physics.

THE UNIVERSE

Speculations about the universe in which men live are as old as human thought and art, as old as the sight of shining stars on a clear night. Yet it was general relativity theory which, only thirty years ago, shifted cosmological problems from poetry or speculative philosophy into physics. We can even fix the year in which modern cosmology was born. It was 1917, when Einstein's paper appeared in the *Proceedings of the Prussian Academy* under the title "Cosmological Considerations in General Relativity Theory."

Although it is difficult to exaggerate the importance of this paper, and although it created a flood of other papers and speculations, Einstein's original ideas, as viewed from the perspective of the present day, are antiquated if not wrong. I believe Einstein would be the first to admit this.

Yet the appearance of his paper is of great importance in the history of theoretical physics. Indeed, it is one more instance showing how a wrong solution of a fundamental problem may be incomparably more important than a correct solution of a trivial uninteresting problem.

Why is Einstein's paper so important? Because it formulates an entirely new problem, that of the structure of our universe; because it shows that general relativity theory can throw new light upon this problem.

The classical physicist thought of our physical space as three-dimensional, our physical time as common to all observers, whether in relative motion or not. These concepts were changed in 1905 when Einstein formulated special relativity theory. The physicist learned that to order physical events it is much more convenient and simple to consider them in a four-dimensional space-time background. Then, in 1916, he found that to understand the phenomena of gravitation he must generalize his concepts once more. In general relativity theory, the universe is represented by a four-dimensional non-Euclidean background, its metric shaped by masses and their motions.

New ideas are born in theoretical physics by the genius and

imagination of men who can look upon an old problem from an entirely new and unexpected point of view. This is how special and general relativity theories were born; this is how quantum theory entered physics. In Einstein's paper on cosmology we see the same ability to look upon old problems in a new way. Yet, as we know today, there is an essential difference. Whereas special and general relativity theories stand in our present day almost as fresh and complete as in the days when they were formulated, whereas in the last thirty years nothing of fundamental importance has been added to Einstein's structure, the problem of cosmology looks very different today from the way it did in the days when Einstein wrote his celebrated paper.

The work on cosmology—that is, on the structure of our universe—appears more than any other in relativity as a cooperative venture. Besides Einstein's name there are others equally important. Let us mention here the Dutch astronomer de Sitter, the Russian Friedmann, the Belgian Lemaitre, the American Robertson. But there are also many others; science does not know racial or national boundaries and scientists all over the world, if allowed to do so, collaborate successfully.

Einstein's original ideas began the science of the structure of our universe. In the hands of others these ideas were later changed and developed under the impact of new observations and new speculations based upon general relativity theory.

What is our over-all picture today?

Summarizing the result of three decades of experimental and theoretical investigations, let us say: *Our universe is a universe of islands*. It consists of islands of matter, or nebulae, in a sea of emptiness.

Imagine that we travel through space, with the greatest *known* and the greatest *possible* speed; that is, with the speed of light. In a matter of minutes we leave the sun behind us. In a matter of hours we leave our entire solar system; in a matter of years we reach the nearest stars. Thus, we judge distances now by light-years, the years that it would take us to traverse these distances while journeying with the speed of light.

Our solar system and all the stars that we see on a bright

night from *our* nearest neighborhood, are a part of *our* galaxy, of *our* nebula; they are a part of the island on which we live. But this galaxy (of which the sun, the planets, the stars visible with the naked eyes are members) is only one of the very many islands, one of the very many nebulae of our universe. Like far-removed islands on a sea, so the nebulae, the great conglomerations of stars, are islands of matter and the sea is empty space. Our galaxy is only one of them. After thousands of years of travelling with the speed of light, we would find ourselves outside our galaxy; then to reach the next nearest island, the nearest conglomeration of stars, we would have to travel almost a million years more! There is nothing fantastic about this; and there is no reason to become disturbed by the extent of emptiness and the rarity of matter in our universe. There is even less reason to become upset about this than about the rarity of gas stations on a desert road, because we shall never travel along these highways of the universe. The light rays that reach our eyes from the distant nebulae are the only messengers that do travel; and they don't mind the emptiness. On the contrary, they could not reach our earth if they were to meet too much absorbing matter on their long voyage.

Let us examine the evidence brought to us by these light messengers and caught by our most powerful reflectors.

Hundreds of thousands of these nebulae-islands have been photographed. The farthest from us which are still visible, though very faint, are about half a billion light-years away from us. This is as far as we can penetrate today. By building better reflectors (like the two-hundred-inch reflector which has recently been completed) we shall be able to penetrate still deeper into space.

The average nebula is about twenty thousand light-years in diameter and the average distance between the nebulae is about two million light-years. I repeat: the nebulae are islands in a sea of emptiness.

The great astronomer E. Hubble gives the following picturesque comparison: imagine tennis balls fifty feet apart scattered through a sphere five miles in diameter. In this comparison a tennis ball stands for a nebula consisting of many millions of stars. The five miles stands for the distance to which we can penetrate today. The fifty feet between the tennis balls tells us how rare matter is and how common empty space is in our universe.

Such is the structure of our universe as a whole, revealed through observation and through simple theoretical interpretations of the observational results.

We are interested in the structure of our universe *as a whole,* that is, in its broad characteristics, in averages, while ignoring small irregularities and cosmologically unimportant deviations. Similarly, when planning an airplane journey around our earth, we are interested in the distribution of landing fields and very little in the villages between them. For such a purpose we consider the earth as a sphere with points representing landing fields. But at other times, while attending to the business of our daily lives, we must care, and we do care, about our neighbors and the happenings in our back yards.

While viewing the universe as a whole we are little interested in the small irregularities, in the fact that each nebula-island has its own peculiar shape, size, age, history. We consider them all alike and disregard the differences in their sizes and in their mutual distances apart. Our picture of *equidistant* nebulae of *equal sizes* is a highly idealized one. As always in science, so here, too, we simplify and idealize; then, as time passes, we usually complicate our original simple picture under the impact of new observations. Still later, these increasing complications make the entire picture so ugly in its complexity that it has to be rejected and a new, simpler picture sought. But in the still-young science of cosmology we have not progressed far beyond the first few steps. Our picture is still very simple; perhaps too simple!

Now we come to the most characteristic and puzzling feature of our island universe. It, too, has been revealed to us by observation. I shall state the result first in technical language. *The spectra of the nebulae show a red-shift.* Or, in less scientific language, *the nebulae seem to run away from us.*

An explanation of our two equivalent statements can be given only in terms of physics.

The pitch of a whistle on an engine that approaches the railway station seems to an observer at the station to be higher than the pitch of the same whistle while the engine stands still. Again, the pitch of the whistle seems lower when the engine travels away from the railway station. This effect, well known in acoustics, is called the *Doppler effect*.

We meet a somewhat similar phenomenon in ordinary life too. Imagine a party travelling by car and dispatching a messenger to you every hour by motorcycle. You will receive the messenger every hour if the party is just resting at a tourist home. But if the car moves away from you, you will receive the messenger at longer time intervals than an hour; if the car moves toward you, you will receive him at time intervals smaller than an hour. As a matter of fact, from the frequency with which the messengers arrive you could deduce the speed with which the party in the car moves toward you or away from you, if you know the speed of the messengers and the frequency with which they are sent to you. The same is true in the case of the engine whistle. The pitch measures the frequency with which the voice-messengers arrive and it is higher (that is, the frequency is higher) if the engine moves toward the station, lower when it moves away from it.

A very similar effect, also well known to the physicist, is the Doppler effect in the field of *optics*.

A spectroscope is an apparatus that analyzes light. For example, if the source of light is a gas through which passes an electric current (as, say, in the case of the neon tube), then what we see, looking at the source through a spectroscope, are thin bright stripes on a dark background. The vapors of different elements give different systems of lines. There are no two elements with two identical systems of lines, just as there are no two men with identical fingerprints. Thus, the system of lines uniquely characterizes the element to which it belongs and every element is characterized by its system of lines.

By analyzing the light from stars or nebulae we can detect

the presence of the same elements that we know and have analyzed on our earth. The lines of hydrogen or helium have the same structure whether they come from our earth, from the sun, from the stars of our galaxy, or from the nebulae.

Yet, if we compare the spectrum of an element on our earth with the spectrum of the same element in a nebula we see the same structure (otherwise we couldn't say that it is the same element), but we also recognize some differences. The whole spectrum—that is, *all* the lines that characterize the element—is slightly shifted. This again, as we know both from theory and experiment, should happen and does happen if the source of light (neon tube, star, nebula) moves away from us or toward us. It is the same effect, the Doppler effect, that we recognized a while ago in the example of the messengers or the engine whistle: the system of lines is shifted toward the *red end* of the spectrum if the source of light moves away from the observer; the lines are shifted toward the *violet end* of the spectrum if the source of light moves toward the observer. The shift toward the red-end indicates a diminished frequency of the light messengers and a shift toward the violet end indicates an increased frequency of the light messengers. As before, in the case of the whistle and the messengers, we can calculate now from such a red or violet shift the speed with which the source of light moves away from us or toward us.

The question arises: why do the nebulae behave as though they were running away from our galaxy? Of course, the simplest answer would be that the nebulae behave as though they were running away from us because they do run away from our galaxy. But then the question is: why do they run?

If the red-shift and the running away of nebulae had been discovered in Biblical times we might have had some explanation that appeared satisfactory. (The nonsensical character of this statement does not escape me!) We could have assumed that in each galaxy there are some planetary systems and that our earth is not the only one populated by so-called intelligent beings. Since our planet is the one on which Adam sinned and the only one on which men kill men, therefore, all the other nebulae have a deeply rooted complex toward our galaxy and try to get as far from us as possible.

Yet we can hardly be satisfied with such an explanation. Even if the inhabitants of other nebulae could see what is happening on our earth, they would see *now* what happened millions of years ago, because light would take millions of years to reach them. Secondly, there is another curious, indeed very curious, point. The red-shift *increases* with the distance. That means, the greater the distance from our galaxy, the greater seems the speed of the running nebulae. This is baffling! Why should the aversion increase with the distance? The law of this increase in red-shift is, in itself, extremely simple: the greater the distance, the greater—proportionately—the red-shift. A nebula a hundred million light-years distant seems to run away from us ten times as quickly as a nebula ten million light-years distant. This law connecting the redshift with the distance seems to be fairly accurate although there appear to be some small systematic deviations. Yet the law is good enough even to allow us to determine the distances of the far-removed nebulae by the very law of the red-shift.

We return to our question. What is the explanation for the law of the red-shift?

In search of an answer, we leave the region of observation and enter the region of speculation, that of general relativity theory. There is a bridge leading to this region of speculation; that is, there is an important principle belonging partially to the field of observation and partially to the field of speculation.

If we look with our reflectors in different directions we see that—statistically—no directions are distinguished. We find, generally, as many nebulae in one direction as in any other. Also, we see that the number of nebulae per unit volume remains constant to any depth to which our reflectors penetrate. Our universe seems to be fairly uniformly filled with matter. Of course, there are some irregularities, but small enough to allow us to assume, with good approximation, that no direction is distinguished and no point in space is distinguished from any other.

Thus, we conclude that our universe is *uniform*. We may

have rushed to such a conclusion too quickly. It seems that all we know is only a fragment of our universe, and the new larger reflector may reveal some irregularities, some systematic deviations from uniformity. This is certainly possible. Yet if we assume that the universe is not uniform we should have to know how it changes in direction and in depth. Obviously, to say that our universe is uniform means to make the simplest possible assumption. Thus we assume (and this is a fundamental hypothesis) the uniformity of our universe, and in doing so we do not contradict experience.

This assumption, gained essentially from observation, was taken over and much sharpened by theory. It became, so to speak, a moral commandment for our universe. We claim: the story of our universe—taken as a whole—must be the same, whether written from our galaxy or from any other nebula. Let us imagine, since there are no limits set to our imagination, that to each nebula we send an observer, each properly equipped with brains and instruments. The history of our universe will be the same for each of these observers. This is what we mean by the principle of uniformity. There will be small irregularities, of course, but a smoothed-out and idealized universe will be reflected in the same way in the scientific descriptions of all these scientists populating different globes in different nebulae.

Now we have a powerful principle restraining the possibilities for the structure of our universe. The model of our universe must conform to the principle of uniformity!

We return to our previous question. How do we explain the red-shift? Now our question becomes more general and more difficult. If we accept the principle of uniformity, then this means that the observer on a nebula outside our galaxy notices the red-shift, too! Thus they do not only run away from us but also from each other.

But even this conclusion is slightly premature. Perhaps the red-shift can be explained in a different way too, and not only by assuming that the nebulae run away from each other. All we do assume at this moment is that each observer, on each of these nebulae, would confirm the existence of the red-shift and that each observer would find that such a redshift is proportional to the distance.

Thus we are led to another question: what are the possible structures of our universe consistent with the principle of uniformity? It is here that the story of the structure of our universe becomes intermingled with the story of relativity theory, more specifically with that of general relativity theory. We ask: what are the possible models of our universe, consistent with the principles of general relativity theory, with the principle of uniformity, and with the observed red-shift?

True enough, the principle of uniformity and the law of the red-shift restrict the possible relativistic models of our universe. Yet, there are still many models possible and the evidence of observation is not sufficiently conclusive to allow a unique choice. But whatever the character of the universe we live in, we know at least that all the possible universes can be divided into two classes. Our universe is either *open* or *closed*. This important statement does not sound too impressive. It may remind you of the trivial fact that a door can also be either open or closed. Yet the recognition of two such possibilities is a great discovery. In the early nineteenth century the statement that the universe is closed would have been meaningless. A Euclidean space was then the only possibility.

What are the characteristic features of an open and of a closed universe?

Let us start with a closed universe. The universe of the two-dimensional creatures living on a sphere would be a closed one. For them, we remember, a light ray sent out returns ultimately to the point of its departure.

Similarly, our universe is possibly a closed universe although it is more difficult to picture than to describe mathematically a three-dimensional spherical space. Yet we can at least imagine in principle a crucial experiment telling us whether our universe is closed or not. Send a light ray into open space. If, after some time, the light ray comes back, then the universe is closed. If it never comes back, then the universe is open. There are, of course, some technical difficulties connected with such an experiment, but we may ignore them. The biggest difficulty is that we have too little time; according to our present knowledge, it would take billions of years for light to navigate our world and come back to us. Yet there is a chance that with the new two-hundred-inch reflector we shall discover, in a roundabout way, whether our universe is open or closed.

We can picture our universe as closed by suppressing one dimension and comparing it to the universe of the two-dimensional creatures living on a sphere. Pursuing this comparison, let us imagine golden points sparsely, but uniformly, distributed through such a sphere; they represent to us the nebulae of our world. What about the red-shift? In answering this question, we must slightly complicate our two-dimensional picture. Imagine that a sphere expands like a balloon under increased pressure. This expanding sphere, rather than a sphere with an unchanged radius, is the two-dimensional model of our universe! We see that such a model satisfies both the principle of uniformity and the law of the red-shift. Indeed: our nebulae—the golden points on the expanding balloon—will remain uniform because they were dotted uniformly and because the expansion preserves the shape of the sphere and changes only its radius. The distances between the nebulae measured on the balloon will increase. An observer on any of these nebulae will see that others recede from him. It is also clear that very near to any chosen nebula the speed of the expansion will appear to the observer proportional to the distance.

We shall examine now the other possibility, that of an open universe. Here it is unnecessary to suppress one dimension and we may return to the three-dimensional picture of our space. It is best to understand this open-type universe from a historical perspective.

Once upon a time all the matter of our universe was concentrated in a very small volume. In our idealized mathematical model we may say that it was concentrated in a point. Thus all the nebulae were squeezed tightly together. Then something happened and the whole world of matter exploded like shrapnel. The nebulae began to run away from each other with constant speed. Thus, judging, for example, from our galaxy, those nebulae which had a greater speed than others moved farther away than others. Today they still move uniformly.

We see why such a history of our universe gives us the law of the red-shift (proportional to the distance) and also satisfies the uniformity principle. The farther away the nebulae are, the greater their speed, because they had this greater speed when the universe was created and they retain this greater speed because they move uniformly. The nebulae nearer to us have smaller speeds because they had smaller speeds at the moment of creation and they retain these smaller speeds. We also see, although this is slightly more difficult, that the principle of uniformity is not violated. Indeed, all the nebulae were once together, and although we can say that they began to run away from our galaxy, the same can be said by the inhabitants of any of these nebulae. The speediest of them would have a speed approaching that of light and the entire matter of the universe would be enclosed inside a sphere with a radius equal to the speed of light c times the epoch t_0 that has passed from the moment of creation. Each observer can draw such a sphere for himself and such a statement will be true for any observer. The transition from one *system* (that is, from one nebula) to another is governed by the transformation formulated by the special theory of relativity, the Lorentz transformation. It tells us how to describe phenomena in one *system* if we know the description in another *system*. Take, for example, our galaxy as a point O and a very far-removed nebula as a point P. Then P will be near the edge S of the sphere with the radius $c\,t_0$ drawn around O. But the observer at P will imagine himself in the center of such a sphere too. All the nebulae between P and S will seem to lie on a contracted shell for the O observer compared with the P observer. This is because they move quickly. It is the result of the contraction of length in the direction of motion as required by special relativity theory. For the same reason all the nebulae farther than O will appear to lie on a contracted shell for the observer in the nebula P. The history of such an open universe would be the same for any observer on any nebula.

It is only by a detailed calculation that we can show more explicitly how both the law of the red-shift and the uniformity principle follow from such a picture.

When was our universe created? From the observation of the present red-shift we can deduce that the expansion started some billions of years ago.

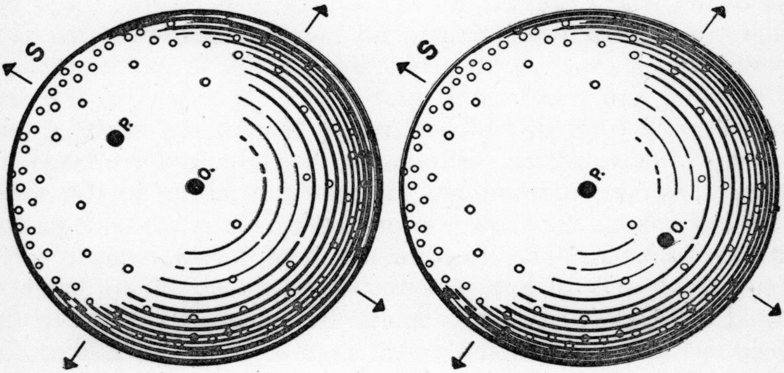

In an open universe, all the nebulae between P and S will seem to lie on a contracted shell for the observer at O compared with the observer at P.

Now, since we know at least in outline the two possible characters of our universe, we may ask: is our universe open or closed? As I said before, there is not enough evidence to answer this question. We may ask a more modest one: would we prefer an open or a closed universe? This is, of course, a subjective question, and different scientists may provide different answers. Yet, I believe that a great majority of those who work on cosmological problems would prefer our universe to be a closed one. There is more mathematical beauty in a closed universe; such a universe is finite although it has no boundary. (The question "what is beyond a three-dimensional sphere" is meaningless; there is no beyond just as there is no beyond for the two-dimensional creatures living on a sphere.) The mathematical superiority of the closed universe is apparent if we consider any physical problem on such a cosmological background. In the open universe we have to worry about happenings at infinity because we have infinities of time and space in such a universe. We don't have them in a closed universe and, if we are allowed to be technical for a moment, the problem of an electromagnetic field, for example, becomes an attractive boundary value problem, fitting much better into the general scheme of modern physical theories than when treated on the background of an open universe.

This century has changed the picture of our world. From atoms to the structure of our universe we see revolutionary changes, a rapid development which can hardly be compared with any other in the short history of mankind. This development has sprung partially from needs, and if we look back it seems essentially determined by the previous state of science. But it would be wrong to assume that the entire development of science is of a utilitarian character. It is not. Many of our speculations about atoms and about our universe were created because of man's curiosity, because of his desire to penetrate deeper and deeper into the unknown. The utilitarian value of many of our theories may be nil, but they help us to comprehend the world we live in.

I have tried to sketch briefly the scientist's efforts to understand the architecture of our universe. These efforts, though linked with observation, are essentially of a speculative character. In the last thirty years we have succeeded in formulating a new problem, in viewing some of the possible solutions, but our answers are neither decisive nor final. Indeed, there are no final or decisive answers in science.

All our cosmological speculations, though they have gone beyond Einstein's original paper, grew from the ideas of relativity theory. In the history of human thought, they represent one of the many paths emanating from a common source: relativity theory, the creation of one man.

CHAPTER FIVE

EINSTEIN'S PART IN THE GREAT UNFINISHED REVOLUTION

THE BIRTH OF QUANTUM THEORY

RELATIVITY theory was created in all its essential features by one man, and its principles stand unchanged today. But relativity theory forms only a comparatively small part of the common effort of all physicists working to build a consistent theory of the phenomena of nature. Almost every physicist would agree that the great revolution which rebuilt the physics of our century lies not in relativity but in *quantum* theory. Its history is the history of our endeavors to understand matter and radiation—that is, the nature and composition of elementary particles from which the world of matter and radiation can be reconstructed. We know now that our material world, the pencil with which I write, my desk, my body, the earth, sun, planets, stars, nebulae, are all built from bricks of matter of a few kinds: electrons, protons, positrons, neutrons, and mesons. Quantum theory deals with the laws that describe how matter is built out of these elementary particles and what the forces are between them as revealed in spectral lines, in radioactive phenomena, or in the process of fission. The story of modern physics is in great part that of quantum theory.

Whereas relativity theory is almost entirely the work of one man pursuing his lonely path, quantum theory is the achievement of many men working independently or together, pursuing step by step our still incomplete knowledge of matter, radiation, and their mutual interaction. It is a fascinating and involved story. If a physicist were asked to quote the most important name in this development he would find it difficult and would much prefer to give a list of names, If you asked him to mention, say, eight physicists whose contributions to quantum theory stand above others, he would probably give you the following list: Planck, Einstein, Bohr, De Broglie, Schroedinger, Heisenberg, Dirac, and Pauli. Each of these men received the Nobel prize for his theoretical work in quantum theory.

Thus, if we say that quantum theory is the great scientific revolution of our century we see that Einstein played a most important, although not a unique, role in it. We cannot describe here the whole revolution brought about in physics by quantum theory. Many books on different levels have been, and will be, written on this subject. We shall be concerned here mainly with Einstein's part in this revolution. But even this subject is too broad, and we shall confine ourselves to discussing only the most important one of Einstein's contributions.

Before we do so we must clarify our picture, for what I have said may have given the impression that there are, so to speak, two distinct streams in modern physics: one, represented by relativity theory, rather a narrow stream, and one broad stream represented by quantum theory. Such a picture would be utterly wrong. Quantum theory is not independent of relativity theory, and one cannot imagine it without the part which relativity theory had in its development.

True enough, the beginnings of quantum theory were independent of relativity theory. They lie in the work of Planck at the turn of our century, five years before Special Relativity was born. Einstein's most important contribution to quantum theory was formulated in a paper that appeared as early as 1905; in the same year and in the same volume of *Annalen der Physik* in which his paper on relativity theory was printed. (As a matter of fact, as we shall see, these were not the only papers of Einstein that appeared in this volume. The Swiss patent office must have been a good place to work.)

Only up to 1905, then, can we treat the story of quantum theory independently of relativity. Later the two stories became intermingled: De Broglie's and Dirac's great works in quantum physics are so intimately connected with relativity theory that they can be treated in books on either subject. If I may use technical language for a moment, I should say that great progress was achieved in quantum theory by making it Lorentz-invariant. This was done in 1928 by Dirac. Another important instance of the intermingling of quantum theory and relativity is atomic energy and its utilization. Here the crucial ideas start with relativity theory, in the connection between mass and energy, but it was quantum theory that revealed the properties of matter and the disintegration of elements that made atomic energy possible. Indeed, the influence of relativity upon quantum theory is a very important chapter in the history of physics. In judging the impact of Einstein's ideas this phase of his far-reaching influence upon modern science must not be forgotten.

In giving an account of Einstein's own role in the great quantum revolution we must once more return to the beginning of our tale, to the year 1905. But even before we do this, we shall have to sketch in the history of the scientific experiments and the theoretical ideas that led to Einstein's discovery. Indeed, for a short while we must go as far back as the seventeenth century to the work of Newton and Huygens.

In the seventeenth century two different theories of light were formulated by two great men, Newton and Huygens. They were the *corpuscular* and the *wave* theories.

Newton's great work, *Optics,* contains descriptions of his experiments on the dispersion of light and a cautious formulation of his corpuscular theory. According to Newton, light behaves as though it consists of corpuscles: weightless particles travelling with the speed of light. There are different kinds of particles belonging to different colors, but in empty space all of them move uniformly along a straight line with the speed of light. In Newton's theory the phenomenon of light is explained by a mechanical picture. Its ingredients are weightless particles and their motion.

But the rival theory of Huygens is also a mechanical one. Formulated at the same time, his theory competed with Newton's for supremacy in the region of optical phenomena. According to Huygens, light is a wave. While talking about a wave we must distinguish between the propagation of the wave and the motion of the particles of matter that form the material medium through which the wave travels. Similarly, while analyzing the routes through which gossip spreads we must distinguish between the spread of the gossip and the motion of a gossiper; she may move from her home to her neighbors and back, but the gossip itself may spread radially in all directions from its source. Similarly, water particles in the case of a water wave move up and down, but the wave caused by a stone dropped in the water moves radially from the source. What is the medium through which the light waves travel, according to Huygens? A weightless, transparent medium permeating the entire universe: the ether. This is how the ether was born.

Once again we return to the concepts from which we started. We must do so because Einstein's great work in quantum theory is concerned with the physics of light while his great work in relativity theory is concerned rather with the geometry of light. This will become clear when we discuss his *light-quanta* or *photons,* but before doing this we must dig deeper into the past.

Whenever we talk about a wave, the important concepts by which we describe it are: the speed with which the wave travels and the wave length. The latter means the distance at a certain moment from a crest to the nearest crest or from a valley to the nearest valley. According to the wave theory of light, different simple colors are characterized by different wave lengths.

Thus we have two different theories, the corpuscular and the wave theory. In the region of our sense impressions we find light of different colors. In the corpuscular language this means light particles of different kinds. In wave language it means light of different wave lengths.

It is disturbing to have two different theories, for it would seem that light can be either a wave or a shower of corpuscles but it cannot be both. Philosophically such a statement is meaningless. The object of a theory is to arrange and to explain events to form a simple picture from which the phenomena and the laws of nature can de deduced. If, in Newton's time, the known phenomena could be explained equally well by both theories then there was no basis for a clear-cut choice between them, which was essentially the situation then. (The last sentence is somewhat of an oversimplification, but we may lose the over-all picture if we try to be too scrupulously exact.) Thus, both theories could be regarded as equally true in the seventeenth and eighteenth centuries. But not so in the nineteenth century, for then the situation changed radically because of the work of Young and Fresnel. A new phenomenon became known and thoroughly investigated, and one of the theories ceased to be acceptable. It was Huygens' theory that emerged victorious in the nineteenth century.

Why?

Because a new phenomenon entered the picture: the diffraction of light.

We shall describe a simple experiment and ask the supporters of corpuscular and of wave theory to predict its outcome. If their predictions differ, and only if their predictions differ, shall we have means at hand to decide between Newton's corpuscular and Huygens' wave theory.

Out of the very many experiments of this kind, we choose one. We have a source of light, before which we place a small circular aperture. What will appear on a screen on which the light falls after having passed through this circular opening?

The answer of the supporter of Newton's corpuscular theory would be something like this:

Particles of light travel along a straight line. They pass through the circular hole and they will travel inside a cone formed by the source of light (which we assume to be a point source) and the lines connecting it with the circular opening.

On the screen we shall see a shadow where the light cannot penetrate and light where it can. The transition from light to shadow will be sharp.

Let us remember this prediction which states that, however small the circular opening is, there will always be the abrupt transition from light to darkness.

But the prediction of the supporter of Huygens' wave theory would be different; he would argue:

Imagine short waves on a river moving toward a big ship. They will not penetrate to the other side of the ship, which will consequently form a shadow. But replace the ship by a small boat or a log of wood and the waves will bend and penetrate to the other side of the obstacle. Thus, you will have distinct shadow or no shadow, depending on whether your obstacles are big or not very big compared with the wave length. If this is true, then something similar will happen in the experiment of projecting light through a circular opening. If you make this opening smaller and smaller, then the time will come when the shadow will not appear. According to my calculations, with which I do not wish to bother you, you will find alternating dark and light rings instead of one area of light and one area of shadow. The transition from light to darkness will be accomplished through these dark and light rings, or perhaps colored rings if your source sends light of different colors; that is, of different wave lengths. Once we can detect such a phenomenon I shall be able to deduce from it and from my calculations how big, or rather how small, is the wave length of the light wave sent by the source. Thus, while my colleague who believes in the Newtonian theory predicts the appearance of light and shadow, I predict for sufficiently small openings the appearance of dark and light or perhaps colored rings. Here lies an essential difference between our two theories.

It was this prediction that proved to be right and it established the reign of the wave theory in the nineteenth century. The phenomenon of diffraction allows us to measure the wave length of light. Of course, compared with human dimensions such a wave length is small, and it was only for this reason that the validity of Newton's corpuscular theory could have been accepted for such a long time. Yet, let us not forget Newton's picture entirely, for we shall see later that Einstein returned to it and put a new breath of life into the dead theory.

Experiments on the diffraction of light allow us to measure the wave lengths of the visible spectrum. Of all the rainbow colors violet has the shortest wave length, red the longest. In the nineteenth and twentieth centuries, this range was extended. X rays were discovered, which are much shorter (in their wave length) than visible radiation, and gamma rays, much shorter than X rays. Now, we also have radio waves, which are much longer than visible radiation. This great range of radiation is covered by one theory: Maxwell's field theory. Such was the state of our knowledge at the turn of our century.

Great ideas and new theories are born through conflicts, from difficulties and contradictions to which no satisfactory outcome appears possible. Such were the conditions that led to the most important physical theories of the twentieth century: quantum and relativity.

The difficulties that lay at the basis of quantum theory are less spectacular and seemed at first less profound philosophically than those that led to relativity theory. The most profound features of quantum theory appear rather in a later stage. In presenting quantum theory from a logical point of view, it would be convenient in part to ignore and to outflank the historical development which in contrast to relativity theory appears rather accidental. But we shall follow the historical pattern here, since the early difficulties influenced Einstein's way of thinking and led to his theory of photons.

What problem of physics gave rise to quantum theory? Let us think about the visible spectrum of the sun. The light emitted by the sun is white, a mixture of all visible colors. We can split this white light into its components by passing it through a prism. Nature does the same for us in the magnificent phenomenon of a rainbow. In the language of wave theory, we can say that in the visible spectrum of the sun we have all wave lengths present, starting with the shortest wave length, that corresponding to the violet, up to the longest wave length, corresponding to red.

The sun is the source of energy and this energy is scattered through waves of different lengths. Every part of the spectrum—that is, every color—carries with it a certain portion of this energy. Let us divide this spectrum, say, in ten parts; that is,

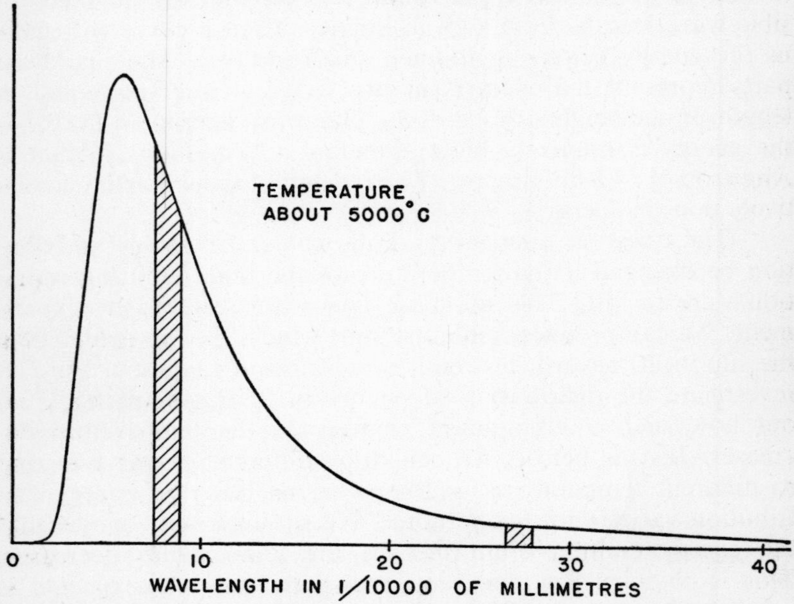

The shadowed parts represent energies in two different intervals, equal in length. The red end of the spectrum is relatively poor in energy.

in ten smaller intervals according to the wave lengths. How much energy will be contained in each of these sections? Will each of them carry one-tenth of the total energy? Even a superficial experiment shows that it does not. The energy is unequally divided among these sections. But what, then, is the law governing this? How much will, say, the third section carry and how much the seventh? What is the distribution of the sun's radiant energy as between the several parts of the spectrum? If we wish to have a more precise knowledge of the distribution of energy in the spectrum, we should divide it into a larger number of parts, say, hundreds or even thousands instead of ten. Our question may then be answered by experiment; this was done in the nineteenth century. The best way to summarize this answer is to draw a graph. On a horizontal line we indicate all the possible wave lengths from zero to infinity. Then a curve will show us the energy belonging to each small interval. The shadowed parts represent the energies in two different intervals equal in length. In the neighborhood of the blue wave length—4,800 *Å*—the energy is relatively most abundant (10 million *Å* [that is Ångstroms] = 1 millimetre.) The red end of the spectrum is relatively poor in energy.

The question then arose: how would the energy distribution be changed if the temperature of the body emitting radiation were to fall? This question, too, was answered by experiment. We can produce miniature suns which, though colder than the sun itself, nevertheless emit every kind of radiation. We can investigate the distribution of energy in their spectra and find out how such a distribution changes as the temperature decreases. Just as before, we can draw different curves referring to different temperatures and showing us how the energy distribution varies with temperature. We see from our curves that the energy emitted diminishes as the temperature decreases. This is obvious. But more interesting and more unexpected is another phenomenon. The strips of the spectrum carrying with them relatively the greatest amount of energy move toward the red parts of the spectrum; that is, toward greater wave lengths. At a temperature of 6,000° C, the greatest energy is around the color blue. At 3,000° C, however, it is markedly nearer the red end. The energy in any part of the spectrum depends upon two factors, the wave length and the temperature of the emitting body; or, putting it mathematically, energy is a function of wave length and temperature.

Up to now, we have merely described the results of experiments and measurements. But how can we explain these results

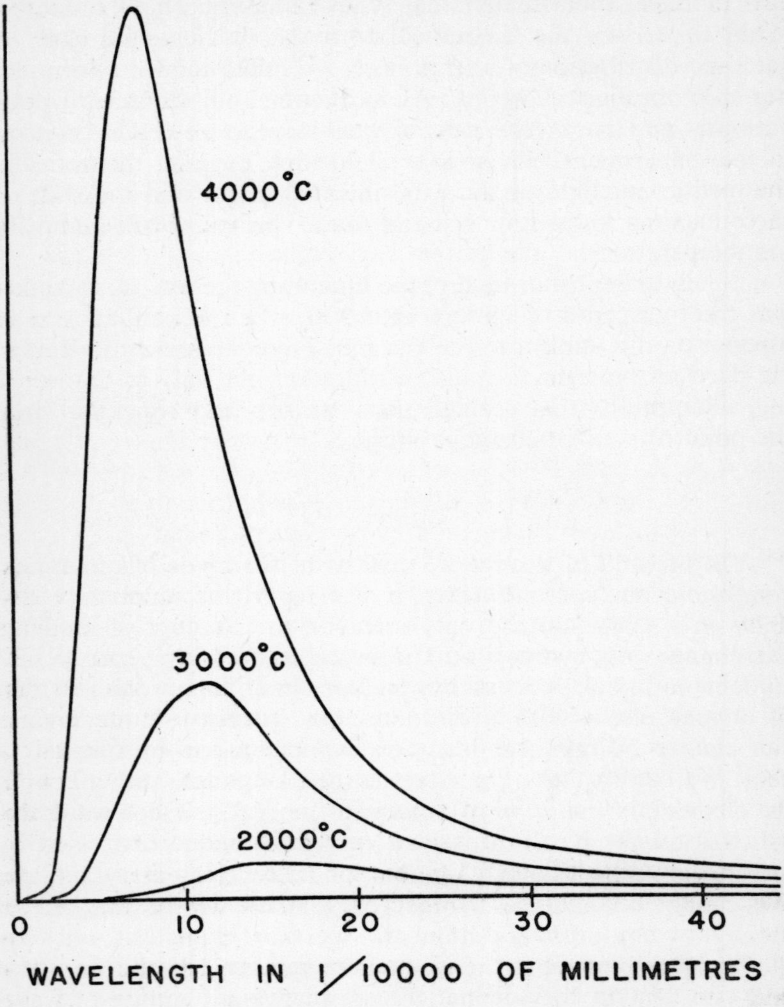

The strips of the spectrum carrying with them relatively the greatest amount of energy move toward the red parts of the spectrum, as the temperature decreases.

theoretically? We knew enough, so the nineteenth-century physicists thought, about matter that sends radiation, about radiation itself, to *deduce* the theoretical formula which would give us the right distribution of energy. Yes, we could deduce a formula, but the formula was wrong. All deductions, all theoretical derivations—and there were many of them—led to results that contradicted experiment. Physicists could not explain theoretically the distinct maxima of the experimental curves and the shift of these maxima toward the red end of the spectrum with diminishing temperature.

This difficulty gave birth to quantum theory. Its birthday was the fourteenth of December, 1900, when Max Planck read a paper on this subject to the German Physical Society in Berlin. He derived the right formula of radiation but only by introducing assumptions that seemed new, strange and shocking from the point of view of classical physics.

QUANTA

In life and in science we deal with two kinds of quantities, *continuous* and *discontinuous*. If you report the number of students in a class you use only integers; the number of students can change only by integers. The statement "Today I had 25.687 students in my class" is utterly meaningless. Your wealth or that of anyone else is also a discontinuous quantity. Your savings can change by one cent but they cannot change by one-half a cent. We can say, using a more learned language, that a cent is the elementary *quantum* of money in the U.S.A. Once we establish this quantum, all American currency can be expressed by an integer indicating the number of these elementary quanta. We cannot change the number of students or the amount of money by an arbitrary number. We can change it only by quanta. One student is the elementary quantum in the first case and one cent in the second. These quantities (number of students and money) cannot change continuously. They can change only discontinuously.

If we travel by train from New York we choose the station

where we end our journey but the possible choices, when written down in terms of distances from Grand Central Station, will vary discontinuously. On the other hand, if we go by car, we can go wherever we wish. All the points now accessible by car along a highway form a continuum. We can change the distances where we stop by as little as we wish.

Thus, in practical life we have continuous and discontinuous quantities. We ask: what are the continuous and what are the discontinuous quantities? The question is meaningless. The same quantity which was regarded as continuous in one case may later be regarded as discontinuous. Or perhaps we can say it better this way: the same concept can be regarded as continuous in the description of some phenomena and as discontinuous in other, more refined phenomena. This should not be too astonishing. If you sell the sand of the Sahara Desert in tons, you can regard it as continuous; but if you compare the shape of two grains of sand under the miscroscope, you can hardly regard it as continuous. Something similar happens in science. Quantities which were regarded as continuous in one case have to be regarded as discontinuous in another. It was quantum theory that taught us to regard as discontinuous certain concepts that were previously regarded as continuous.

Let us now discuss the continuous or discontinuous character of the principal physical concepts.

Time is a continuous concept. Periods of time may change by an arbitrarily small number.

Space is continuous. Distances may change by an arbitrarily small number.

Energy is continuous, according to classical mechanics. It can increase or decrease by an arbitrarily small number.

In passing, remember that the chosen unit of energy is one erg, the work accomplished by one dyne along a path of one centimetre. One dyne is the force that accelerates one gram by one centimetre per second per second. Perhaps it is sufficient to remember, omitting the above technicalities, that an erg is a very small unit of work well suited for a description of the work of ants and flies but badly suited for the description of the work of a horse or of water pouring over a T.V.A. dam. By this I mean that the work in these cases if described in ergs would be represented by uncomfortably large numbers.

Thus, late in the nineteenth century, time, space and energy were regarded as continuous.

What about *mass*? Of course, in classical mechanics mass was also regarded as continuous. In everyday experience, in our household economy, we picture arbitrary changes in the amount of butter on our table. Yet the great progress of science in the nineteenth century lies in the recognition of the atomic structure of matter; in understanding that every element consists of atoms, that an atom is the elementary quantum for this element. So, for example, the atom of hydrogen has the mass of

0.000000 000000 000000 0000017 grams.

And we cannot change the mass of hydrogen by any amount smaller than that. Thus, the elementary quantum of hydrogen is small but it is finite. This was a great discovery, a picture very different from the Newtonian one in which mass was regarded as continuous.

From early youth Einstein was very much impressed by the new atomic picture that had emerged in the nineteenth century. While discussing the atomic structure of matter, it is right to digress and to mention, though briefly, another of Einstein's contributions which has nothing to do with relativity or quantum theory. I refer to Einstein's work that appeared in 1905 in the same seventeenth volume of *Annalen der Physik*, in which there are three of Einstein's papers; the one about relativity theory, the one about the photoelectric effect to which we shall return shortly, the third about *Brownian motion*. The last is less important than the other two. In the paper on Brownian motion, Einstein looked for some phenomena that would so clearly demonstrate the atomic structure of matter that even the greatest skeptic would be convinced. Thus he foresaw and described the phenomenon of Brownian motion, a phenomenon which must appear if matter has granular structure. Einstein did not know that such a phenomenon had been known for eighty years. Thus he gave the theory of Brownian motion without knowing that Brownian motion had been observed.

In 1827 Brown noticed that granules of plants, organic or inorganic particles, or any matter pulverized so that the length of each particle is about 1/5000th of an inch, appear agitated if thrown into water and looked at through a microscope. These particles, or, as they are called, the *Brownian particles,* move constantly, travelling in fantastically broken paths. They never stop; their motion never dies out.

Einstein foresaw that such a phenomenon must occur because of the atomic structure of matter. The water, or any other medium into which these particles are thrown, consists of elementary quanta of matter in constant motion, pushing around the Brownian particles. The Brownian motion constitutes, so to speak, a magnification of the restlessness of the small particles of water so that we can see through the microscope the result of the granular structure of water and the result of the constant bombardments of Brownian particles by the particles of water. Indeed, the study of Brownian motion and the knowledge of its theory as developed by Einstein allows us to find out something about the mass of the bombarding particles. A while ago, I quoted the mass of the hydrogen atom. Experiments on Brownian motion and the theory as formulated by Einstein allow us to find this value!

I mention here only briefly the story of Brownian motion and its theory as formulated in Einstein's beautiful paper. My aim is to stress Einstein's influence upon our modern civilization, and in this connection the story of Brownian motion is not very important. Independently of Einstein, a great Polish scientist, Smoluchowski, my professor at Cracow, formulated the theory of Brownian motion almost at the same time as Einstein did. He spent a great part of his short life on the study of the atomic structure of matter.

Yet what is important in this story is that besides the general, almost philosophical, problems that led to relativity theory and to theories about the structure of our universe, Einstein was fascinated by the atomic structure of matter. Although, as we have seen, Einstein's papers on diverging subjects appeared in one year, it is obvious to every scientist that they were the result of years of work and thought.

To finish with the discontinuous structure of matter, let us simply state that at the end of the nineteenth century the atomic theories were generally accepted by scientists.

Is *electricity* continuous or discontinuous? Like mass, electricity was regarded as continuous in the early development of science. But again, late in the nineteenth century, the discovery of the electron forced us to change our picture. Electrons are the smallest quanta of negative electricity. Unfortunately, for positive electricity we have two elementary quanta, the heavy protons and the light positrons. These quanta of electricity are at the same time the bricks of which atoms are composed. In the twentieth century we discovered that the atom is not an elementary quantum of matter, that it is built of elementary bricks: electrons, protons, positrons, neutrons, mesons. The story of how these atoms are composed of such bricks is essentially that of quantum theory.

We mentioned before three quantities that were regarded as continuous in classical physics: time, space, energy. Quantum theory, which later became the theory of the structure of atoms, began with Planck's discovery. We can now formulate Planck's great achievement: he took energy from the class of continuous concepts and shifted it into the class of discontinuous concepts.

Energy, like mass, like electricity, has a granular structure!

You remember that Planck's aim was to find the right law for radiation, that all classical assumptions invariably led to the wrong law. By assuming that energy can be emitted or absorbed only in quanta, Planck deduced the right law of radiation, splendidly confirmed by experiment. It was this success that started quantum theory. Later, the phenomena confirming the granular structure of energy were so numerous that quantum theory became the everyday tool of every physicist.

We ask now: what is the elementary quantum of energy? The question is not simple to answer. In the U.S.A., the elementary quantum of money is one cent. A statement that I have one one-hundredth of a cent in a bank is meaningless. Yet in Greece the elementary quantum is one drachma, which, at this moment, is one one-hundredth of a cent. Thus, a Greek who has accumulated one drachma can say that he has one ten-thousandth of a dollar.

Have you ever read Robert Louis Stevenson's story "The Bottle Imp"? Here a man buys a bottle to save his wife's life. He can perform miracles with it, but if he still has it when he dies, his soul will belong to the devil. Thus, he has to perform his miracle quickly and sell the bottle. He must also sell it for a price smaller than he bought it for. These are the rules of the game and if he violates them the bottle will chase him. The entire plot is based on the fact that there is an elementary quantum of money, and the plot would have been meaningless if money were a continuous quantity. The poor man who wants to save his sick wife's life buys the bottle for one farthing, selling his soul to the devil. He confides his troubles to his well-educated wife, who finds a solution. They move to French islands where five French cents are equivalent to one farthing and they get rid of the bottle. Since Stevenson lived in a stable world, the story ends there.

Similarly, in the case of energy, there is not one quantum of energy, but many quanta of energy. The sun or any other body emits or absorbs radiation. True, it does this in quanta, but the size of the quantum will depend upon the wave length of the radiation that it emits or absorbs. The shorter the wave length, the bigger the quantum. Red radiation has a wave length twice as big as violet radiation. Thus matter emits or absorbs violet radiation in portions—that is, quanta—twice as big as for red radiation. The energy quanta of X rays (small wave length) are bigger than those of the visible spectrum. Thus, if we now determine the size of the quantum, say, for the red end of the spectrum, we shall know how big, or rather how small, it is for any other radiation. Of course, the energy quantum will be very small, otherwise radiation's granular structure could not have been hidden for such a long time. One erg, a very small unit of energy, contains 400,000 million quanta belonging to red radiation and 200,000 million quanta belonging to violet radiation. Indeed, the quanta are small.

How will you find the quantum of energy belonging to radiation of a particular wave length? Here are Planck's directions: divide the speed of light (30 000 000 000 centimetres per second) by the wave length expressed in centimetres and multiply it by *Planck's constant,* denoted always and everywhere by h. You will get the elementary quantum of energy in ergs belonging to this particular radiation. What is h? The answer is:

$$h = 0.000000\ 000000\ 000000\ 000000\ 00655.$$

Of course, it is a small number because the quanta of energy are small. (Planck's constant (h) has the dimensions of erg $\times$ second. The "dimension" tells us how to change the number representing h if we change the units of energy and time.)

Thus, a new revolutionary idea was introduced into physics and with it a discrepancy between theory and experiment was removed. It was one of the most fruitful ideas in all the history of science.

Before we go on from here to Einstein's work, a word about the philosophical implications of Planck's discovery. As always in the history of physics, we had to change our fundamental assumptions because we wished to account for the growing richness of our experiences. A long chain of reasoning leads from these assumptions to the derivation of the right formula for radiation. In modern physics the chain of deductions leading from assumptions to conclusions that can be verified by observation grows longer and longer. The development of science is a biological process. We are continually forced to change our assumptions if we wish to understand the world in which we live.

PHOTONS

Planck's ideas lacked decisiveness. They were the beginning of a movement to which Einstein gave a new impetus because he had the courage and independence to draw new and far-reaching conclusions.

In Einstein's work on quantum theory, we recognize the

same characteristic feature that we saw before: originality. Revolutions are created by men with vision who see clearly the flaws in the old order and have the courage to break with tradition, by men who care far more for understanding than knowledge. Planck's theory was known to Einstein; though he recognized its importance he was aware that it was like a makeshift device, just to get one formula: the dependence of radiation energy upon wavelength and temperature. This it did splendidly.

The wave theory of light deals with radiation. In its early form Planck's quantum theory deals with emission and absorption. Imagine that radiation with a definite wavelength falls on a body that absorbs it; then this absorption occurs in quanta. The body swallows morsels of such radiation, each of a definite size. What Einstein did was to change fundamentally the picture of radiation itself. Let us, at least for the moment, discard the wave theory of light. Assume with Einstein that light itself possesses granular structure, that it consists of grains, of bullets, of quanta speeding through space with the velocity of light. How similar is this picture to that of Newton's corpuscular theory! In a certain sense Einstein revived Newton's corpuscular theory, though his concepts now have a depth they could not have had in the time of Newton. The original, primitive form of Newton's theory will be changed, its scope will be deepened. Yet, the essential ideas will be very similar. The grains of the energy of light, the so-called *photons*, will take the place of Newton's corpuscles. Thus light, according to Einstein, is a shower of photons, and the photon is the elementary quantum of energy.

Yet Einstein, while reviving Newton's theory, does not abandon the wave theory of light. The phenomenon of diffraction and the successes of the wave theory of light are too important to allow him to do so. Einstein not only revives the Newtonian theory but also builds a bridge between Huygens' theory and Newton's. It is as though Einstein were reconciling the two old foes by letting them look upon phenomena from a higher level of understanding.

This period of Einstein's work on the quantum theory of radiation is revolutionary but at the same time conciliatory.

There is no contradiction in this. His theory of light reconciles the views of Huygens and Newton, but this reconciliation is accomplished through the introduction of new and revolutionary ideas.

What Einstein says in essence is that we can successfully describe some light phenomena in wave terminology, but we can describe some others successfully in a corpuscular or photon terminology. We can translate certain sentences from one terminology to the other, just as we can translate the Bible from one language to another. Here are some examples:

Terminology of the Wave Theory	*Terminology of the Quantum Theory*
1. The visible spectrum contains waves of varying lengths.	1. The visible spectrum contains photons of varying energies.
2. The wave length of the red end of the spectrum is twice the wave length of the violet end.	2. The photon energy for the red end of the spectrum is half of that for the violet end.
3. Homogeneous radiation has a definite wave length.	3. Homogeneous radiation consists of photons of equal and definite energy.

On the left-hand side of our miniature dictionary, we have the word "wave length"; wave length is measured in centimetres. On the right-hand side we have the word "photon energy." Photon-energy is measured in ergs. The essential element of Einstein's theory is not only the new corpuscular or rather the photon picture but also the bridge, the transition from the concept of wave length to that of photon energy. To every wave length there is a corresponding photon energy, to every photon energy a corresponding wave length. The formula for this transition is the same as given before by Planck, but Einstein applies it now to photons; it is still, even today, the most elementary and important formula in quantum theory: velocity of light divided by wave length and multiplied by Planck's constant gives the energy of the corresponding photon. This formula bridges wave and quantum theories of radiation.

Let us review quickly the region of radiation and forget the wave theory. Let us look upon radiation as a shower of photons. Radio waves are composed of photons of very small energy (in the language of wave theory, the wave length is comparatively large). They can be likened to pellets of cotton or wool. Then there is the visible spectrum. Its photons are like revolver bullets. The photons of ultraviolet radiation are like rifle bullets. Then, X rays are like a shower of shells from big guns.

What is the justification for this new corpuscular picture? Are there any experimental facts that can be explained by Einstein's theory of radiation but not by the wave theory? There are! Here we shall deal only with the simple phenomenon known as the *photoelectric effect*.

Imagine a wall built along the seashore. A sea wave impinges upon the wall, washing away some of its surface, retreats, and a new wave comes in. The mass of the wall decreases and we may ask how much of the wall is washed away in, say, one year. But let us change the picture and imagine that someone is shooting at the wall and splinters of the wall fall away when a bullet hits the wall. Again, the mass of the wall decreases and we can well imagine, say, that in one year the same reduction of mass can be achieved by shooting as by the incoming waves. Yet, from the appearance of the wall we could easily detect by which of these two processes the mass of the wall was decreased: whether by sea waves or by the shower of bullets. It would be good to keep these two different pictures in mind while discussing the photoelectric effect.

Now, the photoelectric effect can be described either in the language of wave theory or in the language of photons. Which of them is more convenient? Which of them leads us to results consistent with experiment? We shall try out both of them and see. Let us start with the wave language.

A light wave of definite wave length—say, ultraviolet light—falls on a metal surface. Experiment tells us that electrons—that is, elementary quanta of electricity (and also the bricks of which matter is built)—are thrown out from the metal plate; the energy of radiation is partially changed into the energy of motion of the expelled electrons. This is the photoelectric effect: light waves throwing out electrons from a metal plate.

Suppose a physicist does not know Planck's quantum theory or Einstein's theory of photons, but knows the wave theory of light. We ask him some questions:

> Q. Do you think that all the electrons have the same energy, that is, the same speed when they leave the metal plate?
>
> A. I don't know, but I don't see why they should. All that I know is that the energy of the ejected electrons cannot be greater than the energy of incoming radiation. This I do know because I believe in the law of conservation of energy.
>
> Q. What will happen if I send out more radiation, if I increase the intensity of the incoming wave? Will the speed of the ejected electrons change?
>
> A. Possibly. More energy comes in, therefore more energy may come out. Either more electrons will be ejected, or their speeds will increase.
>
> Q. Would the photoelectric effect occur if I sent violet light instead of ultraviolet light?
>
> A. I think so. Why not? If the same energy comes in, the same energy should come out in one form or another.

We see that the answers are vague, inconclusive and, as we shall see later, even wrong. Let us now change the picture. Our guide will now be Einstein's theory of photons and we shall ask the same questions again.

> Q. Do you think that all the electrons have the same energy, that is, the same speed when they leave the metal plate?
>
> A. Definitely. We bombard the metal plate with identical bullets; a lucky hit throws out an electron, changing the energy of one photon bullet into the energy of motion

of one electron bullet. Since all photon bullets have the same energy, all electron bullets must have the same energy, too, therefore the same speed.

Q. What will happen if I send out more radiation, if I increase the intensity of the incoming wave? Will the speed of the ejected electrons change?

A. You will increase the number of lucky hits, therefore more electrons will come out, but each of them will have the same energy, that is, the same speed.

Q. Would the photoelectric effect occur if I sent violet light instead of ultra-violet light?

A. This means that now you will bombard the metal plate with smaller bullets. Again, each shot will tear out an electron, but each of these electrons will have a smaller energy because the bombarding photon had a smaller energy. On the other hand, replace ultraviolet light with X rays and each of the electrons will have a greater speed.

We see that according to Einstein's corpuscular theory definite answers can be given to each of these questions. What did the experiment say? It splendidly confirmed all these answers. Einstein's photon theory became established in science.

Not only did experiment confirm Einstein's theory, but it allowed the exact measurement of Planck's constant (h), so important in quantum theory. This was done in 1915, ten years after Einstein's paper appeared. It is not easy to perform such a measurement, but it is easy to explain the idea behind it. According to Einstein's theory, the energy of the photon is equal to the energy of the thrown-out electron. The energy of the electron and, therefore, the energy of the photon can be measured. But the energy of the photon equals Planck's constant multiplied by the speed of light and divided by the wave length. The wave length can be measured through the phenomenon of diffraction and, thus, the only unknown is Planck's constant. This was how Millikan determined this constant, and for this beautiful experimental work he received the Nobel prize two years after Einstein had received this award for the theory of the photoelectric effect.

The story of Einstein's contributions to quantum theory is not devoid of ironical twists. In his work on relativity theory, Einstein is much influenced by the field theory, more specifically by Maxwell's field theory governing the optical and electromagnetic phenomena. He believed, and still believes, that the field view is perhaps the greatest human achievement in science. More than once did Einstein tell me how much more highly he regarded Maxwell's accomplishment than his own. I am sure that history will prove Einstein's self-evaluation to be too modest. It seems strange that, on the one hand, he admired the field theory, based his ideas of relativity on it, and, on the other hand, he seems to have done his best to destroy this field view in his theory of the photoelectric effect. But to draw this conclusion is worse than an oversimplification. It is a falsification.

The principal landmarks in the development of the theory of light were:

1. The wave and the corpuscular theories of light. (Huygens and Newton)
2. The phenomenon of diffraction and the victory of the wave theory. (Fresnel, Young)
3. The electromagnetic theory of light. (Maxwell)
4. The quantum theory of radiation. (Einstein)

Can modern physics discard the wave theory and accept only the quantum theory of radiation? Obviously not. We could then explain the photoelectric effect but not the diffraction of light. We could not explain the appearance of alternating light and dark patterns when light passes through small apertures and when it bends around small obstacles. This seems to be a critical state of affairs. We have two theories—of waves and photons—each of which explains certain facts. The phenomenon of diffraction seems to contradict the photon theory. The photoelectric effect seems to contradict the wave theory. What is the way out of this dilemma? What is light really? Is it a shower of photons or waves in the ether?

These are new and deep questions. They were provoked by Einstein's great discovery and they lead straight into the heart of quantum theory, into the problem of its statistical character, into the question of determinism or indeterminism. A great literature arose around these very questions, important both scientifically and philosophically. Different views were expressed and it is impossible to clarify them without going deeply into the entire conceptual structure of quantum theory.

We are tempted to insist that light can be either a wave or a shower of photons. But the question "What is light really?" is meaningless. Its apparent meaning was based on the now shattered belief that one picture, one theory, is sufficient to explain all phenomena. At least, for the present, we must use two pictures, the corpuscular and the wave picture.

There is no reason to become upset or mystical about it. We can imagine a situation in ordinary life in which it is convenient to use two different theories for the description of one and the same "reality."

Imagine a man who becomes alternately completely blind or completely deaf, but never both at the same time. He is taken to a movie regularly. If he sees it in the period of his deafness, he sees a silent film. If he hears it in the period of his blindness he may think that he is listening to phonograph records. He can explain the world of his sense impressions consistently by two entirely different mechanisms which he may some day combine in one picture. Then he will recognize that the reason for these two different impressions lies in his own limitations, in the fact that he has at his disposal only one of the two senses of hearing and seeing.

Einstein's discovery influenced the further development of quantum theory. In Bohr's picture of the atom, an electron jumps from one state to another and in each jump *emits one photon.* This concept, that utilizes Einstein's photon theory, lies today at the foundations of quantum theory together with other entirely new and most important ideas. Later, De Broglie's work was inspired and influenced by that of Einstein. If light reveals its corpuscular and wave aspect, isn't the same true for a shower of electrons? Here we know the corpuscular aspect, but, following Einstein's argument, we should look for phenomena in which matter reveals its wave aspect. It was this idea that led to the prediction and discovery of diffraction of the waves of matter. Not only was De Broglie's work inspired by Einstein's, but, more than that, Einstein was the first to recognize the importance and freshness of De Broglie's ideas. Schroedinger's work is connected logically with that of De Broglie as the term "wave mechanics" shows. But Schroedinger's work fits only the frame of classical mechanics. According to special relativity theory, every law of physics must be formulated in any inertial frame, and all these frames are connected by the Lorentz transformation. Putting it more technically, the laws of physics must be invariant not with respect to the Galileo but with respect to the Lorentz transformation. Yet, Schroedinger's wave mechanics was not invariant with respect to the Lorentz transformation. A deeper insight was achieved by Dirac, who reconciled quantum and relativity theory, at the same time accomplishing a better agreement between theory and experiment. His theory led to the discovery of new bricks of matter: the positron with a mass equal to that of an electron and with a charge of an opposite sign. The positron is a child of a lawful marriage between quantum and relativity theories.

While writing these pages I am myself astonished at the great influence of Einstein's work upon quantum theory. Its source is both Einstein's corpuscular theory of light and his relativity theory. Yet I have left out many of Einstein's contributions to quantum theory, such as the Einstein-Bose statistics, the quantum theory of specific heat, and others. And any one who follows the present development of quantum theory knows that this influence is far from being exhausted. It is still growing.

There is also irony in Einstein's leadership of the great revolution, for Einstein later turned his back on the revolution that he helped to create. With the passing of time he feels further and further away from the younger generation of scientists, most of whom work in quantum theory. In his life as in his scientific work, he is aloof. There is no bitterness in him, but he does not find to his taste the fruits of the great revolution.

From Einstein's point of view the revolution got out of hand. To understand his attitude we must understand his work and his taste in science. Einstein's views are always worthy of the highest respect, yet they are not the only possible views and they are not shared by the majority of scientists today.

If we look upon Einstein's work we see in it an attempt to form a general theory out of a few principles. This is evident in the special and general relativity theories, where the logical structure is simple and the assumptions can be stated clearly and explicitly. Once these theories were built there was little to change. Einstein's papers on relativity are today not antiquated.

The situation is different in quantum theory. Here we know a tremendous number of facts. Experimental physics is today ahead of theory. Especially in the field of nuclear phenomena we have not one theory but rather a patchwork of many partially contradictory pictures. We are still looking for a general theoretical framework into which we can fit all the known facts. We do not shy away from making quick and new assumptions, from formulating theories that die quicker than flowers. Einstein believes that the modern development in quantum theory is temporary and that it will be replaced by a theory built along different lines; he believes that the great revolution is unfinished.

Once I asked Einstein: "Why are you so dissatisfied with quantum theory, especially with the development that really started from your own work?" Einstein said, "Yes, I may have started it but I always regarded these ideas as temporary. I never thought that others would take them so much more seriously than I did."

Einstein dislikes the statistical character of quantum theory, the assumption that quantum theory deals with laws referring to crowds and not to individuals. This statistical character of modern quantum theory is regarded by many physicists as essential and it seems to them very unlikely that it will change in the future. Einstein is almost isolated in his belief that it will. In recent years he has still gone on with his work along his own lonely path and his influence upon the contemporary development of quantum theory is almost non-existent. No one knows what will happen in the future. But no physicist doubts that for many years to come the historian of science will have no difficulty in tracing in the dramatic development of quantum theory the imprint of Einstein's genius.

CHAPTER SIX

BEYOND THE REVOLUTIONS

THE SEARCH FOR UNITY

WE HAVE seen how relativity theory, essentially the work of one man, changed our concepts of space, time, mass, energy, gravitation, and the geometry of the world. On the other hand, quantum theory is the work of many men, of whom Einstein is one of the most illustrious; his contributions, especially his theory of photons, have not withered away with time.

I have tried to explain in simple words some of Einstein's ideas: those that can be explained simply and those that, more than others, have influenced the science of our century.

One may wonder why we have only rarely referred to Einstein's work after 1921. All Einstein's basic ideas on relativity and quantum theory were the fruits of his earlier years. Yet Einstein has worked, thought, and written scientific papers throughout his life. He thinks about the problems of physics incessantly.

Indeed, after 1921 and up to the present day, Einstein has repeatedly tackled a deep and difficult problem, building and rebuilding theories, rejecting them and starting anew, temporarily satisfied with his results and discarding them when they do not live up to his high standards of logical simplicity and beauty. He is still working on this problem today. His tenacity in sticking to a problem for years, in returning to the problem again and again—this is the characteristic feature of Einstein's genius. As

I have mentioned, Einstein kept returning to the problem of motion for over twenty years until it was finally solved. The other problem over which Einstein pondered for more than twenty-five years still remains unsolved. Will it ever be solved?

In general relativity theory we saw that the *geometrical* field is also the *gravitational* field. The field equations of general relativity theory are the field equations of this gravitational or geometrical field. Such a field is determined by given masses, their known speeds, and also by the *electromagnetic* field. In general relativity theory the masses, their velocities and the electromagnetic field, produced by moving charged particles, all appear as a part of physics. But the gravitational field is different. It, and it alone, characterizes the geometry of our world. Einstein and, perhaps, even earlier, Hermann Weyl, one of the greatest contemporary mathematicians, regarded this difference between the gravitational and electromagnetic fields as something artificial. General relativity theory treats these two fields in entirely different ways. The gravitational field is a geometrical field, too. There is, so to speak, a physical and a geometrical aspect of the gravitational field, but there is only the physical aspect of the electromagnetic field.

The electromagnetic field *is* a field and it should be possible to interpret it geometrically, too. On the other hand, masses and their velocities are strange concepts, fitting badly into the frame of a field theory. They are the remnants of the old Newtonian physics. From the point of view of a field theory, instead of saying "Here is a particle," one should rather say "Here is a region where the field is very strong." Instead of saying "A particle moves," one should rather say "The field changes in time and the region where the field is strong moves." There is no place for the concept of particles and their motion in a pure field theory, and there is no place for the electromagnetic field that cannot be interpreted as a geometrical field as well. Thus general relativity theory, mixing its field and matter aspects, treating gravitational and electromagnetic fields differently, should be regarded only as a temporary structure. A truly unitary field theory ought to include in one unitary field system both the equations of the gravitational and those of the electromagnetic field, all of them necessary for the characterization of the geometry of our world. The concepts both of particles and their motion should be retained in a unitary field theory as concepts of regions in which the field is strong, and the changes of such regions in time and space.

As time went on, the demands made upon the unitary field theory became more and more stringent. When the historical development later emphasized the importance of quantum theory, the program of a general unitary theory became broader and broader. Nowadays from a consistent field theory we would have to regain not only the gravitational equations and those of the electromagnetic field but also the equations for elementary particles which are governed by quantum theory. Is such an ambitious plan possible of realization? Many physicists think that it is not, but Einstein thinks that it is. Although Einstein is not completely isolated in his beliefs (they are shared by Shroedinger too, for example) the majority of physicists regard these attempts as too formal and too speculative.

Yet this is the problem on which Einstein has worked, with a few collaborators, for the last quarter of a century, always pursuing his own ways, not reconciled to the turn that physics has recently taken toward achieving quick results while ignoring the great cosmic problems.

If we view the influence of Einstein's work upon our modern thought we see how great his influence is. Yet if we view all the labors of Einstein, all his scientific output, we are astonished that only a comparatively small part of this work influenced the development of science. How many papers Einstein wrote: ingenious papers, the results of work, thought, work and more work! Yet he himself would now regard some of them as antiquated, wrong, or artificial! When I discussed this very problem with Einstein, he said: "Man has little chance." A scientist is like someone who fires ammunition aimlessly and is astonished when he scores a hit. Few, if anyone, scored as many hits in the entire history of physics as Einstein did. But to assume that men like Einstein do not waste their ammunition means to misunderstand the character of scientific creation and the smallness of man's chance.

THE PHILOSOPHER AND THE MAN

Einstein is regarded not only as a great physicist but also as a great philosopher. He too regards himself as a philosopher. Often he has said to me, "I am more a philosopher than a physicist." Years ago, I listened in Prague to Professor Sommerfeld's lecture at a Physical Society meeting. He spoke to a large audience: "I asked Einstein, whom I consider as the greatest living philosopher, 'Is there any reality outside of us?' And Einstein answered, 'Yes, I believe in it.' "

To say that Einstein is a philosopher is not sufficient. The statement may be misleading, for the word philosophy is often used in at least two different meanings. First it stands for the speculative philosophy which was the only philosophy up to the nineteenth century and its history is connected with names like Kant, Hegel and Bergson. This philosophy has very little if anything to do with Einstein. It is based on the belief that some questions about the existence and nature of our external world are not meaningless—that there is sense in talking about being, not being, that some statements are "synthetic *a priori*." These philosophers use long words discussing intuition, imagination, the thing in itself, trying to express in words the inexpressible world of experiences and beliefs.

But there is also another meaning of the word philosophy accepted by the school of modern philosophers known under the name of logical positivists, or logical empiricists. According to this school, philosophy is not a science in itself but an activity of clarification and there are no purely philosophical problems. They either belong to other regions of human thought or they are meaningless. Traditional philosophy, that is, the speculative philosophy, dealt, in the old times, with those problems that were later absorbed by science, by physics, mathematics, biology, psychology. To the logical positivist a philosopher in the modern sense is a man interested in the foundations of our knowledge, in the clarification of its basic concepts.

It is only in this sense that Einstein can be called a philosopher, and in this sense he is one of the greatest that ever lived. Problems on which philosophers had idly speculated, problems of time, space, and geometry, were absorbed into the field of physics because of Einstein's work. The foundations of physics became clearer; meaningless concepts of ether and of an inertial coordinate system were discarded. Physics became more rational, and empty philosophical speculations were exposed. In this sense Einstein's work belongs to philosophy, and in this sense there is hardly a well-defined line of demarcation between physics and philosophy.

Einstein regards all physical concepts as free creations of the human mind. Science is a creation of the human mind, a free invention. This freedom is restricted only by our desire to fit the increasing wealth of our experiences better and better into a more and more logically satisfactory scheme. This dramatic struggle for understanding seems to go on forever. The history of science teaches us that, although through revolutionary progress we may solve old difficulties, in the long run we always create new ones. We move from complexity towards simplicity because of new and unexpected ideas. Then the evolutionary process begins again, leading to new difficulties and new contradictions. Thus we see in the history of science a chain of revolutions and evolutions. But there are no retreats! As though travelling on a spiral, we reach higher and higher levels of understanding, through the consecutive steps of revolutionary and evolutionary changes.

What does our science express? Is it the structure of our external world? Is there an external world? The idealist would say, "No, the external world radiates from my mind." The realist would say, "Yes, an external world exists." The logical positivist would say, "The question is meaningless and I refuse to answer meaningless questions." What would Einstein's answer be? We do not need to guess because we have it in his own words. In his essay *The World As I See It* Einstein wrote in 1929:

> "The most beautiful thing we can experience is the mysterious. It is the source of all true art and science. He to

whom this emotion is a stranger, who can no longer pause to wonder and stand rapt in awe, is as good as dead: his eyes are closed. This insight into the mystery of life, coupled though it be with fear, has also given rise to religion. To know that what is impenetrable to us really exists, manifesting itself as the highest wisdom and the most radiant beauty which our dull faculties can comprehend only in their most primitive forms—this knowledge, this feeling, is at the center of true religiousness. In this sense, and in this sense only, I belong in the ranks of devoutly religious men."

Einstein is well aware that from the purely rational point of view the sentence, "What is impenetrable to us really exists," is meaningless. But such a sentence has meaning if raised from the rational level of beliefs and convictions to the emotional level of experiences and religious feelings. It is impossible to talk rationally on this level, and all I can do is to quote Einstein's words. Indeed, they represent Einstein's religious beliefs which have some affinity to those of Spinoza.

Einstein influenced our contemporary world because of his doctrine, because of his thoughts and because of his written words. He was never born to be a man of action. Yet I wonder if there is in the history of science any other man who has appealed so much to the imagination of people all over the world as Einstein did. If we wish to have a full picture of Einstein's influence upon our world we must not omit his influence as a man.

Einstein was born on March 14, 1879, in Germany, nine years after Bismarck defeated France and united Germany, nine years after the French Commune. He lived through the flourishing of German imperialism and through its defeat. He saw it flourishing again and then defeated once more.

How important is Einstein's life story for the understanding of Einstein? Books have been written about genius. Endless discussions have been held to decide in what degree a genius is formed by heredity or environment. Although I do not know the literature on this subject, I am inclined to think that the problem is to a great degree meaningless. Even if it were possible to distinguish between heredity and environment I do not see how any rules could be applied to a genius. It seems to me equally silly to try to give a definition of a genius. Genius is a very rare phenomenon. It is characterized just by the fact that it escapes classification. There isn't any other common denominator of genius. This, as I see it, is its only characteristic feature. To be more specific: I worked for a few years with Einstein and during this time I had the unforgettable experience of observing and admiring him. I believe I know and understand him as well as anyone does. For another four years, through the pages of history, I studied and tried to understand the working of another genius, Evariste Galois. Whatever definition of a genius one might give, there seems little doubt that both Galois and Einstein would be regarded by every scientist as geniuses. Yet they seem as different from each other as two men can be. In the tragic life of Galois we see the strong ties by which he was bound to the society in which he lived. He was caught, as in a deadly spider net from which there was no escape. He suffered from the impact of the external world, from its injustice; his heart bled and his life burned out quickly. How different from him is Einstein! His heart never bleeds and he moves through life with mild enjoyment and emotional indifference. For Einstein, life is an interesting spectacle that he views with only slight interest, never torn by the tragic emotions of love or hatred. He is an objective spectator of human folly. and feelings do not impair his judgments. His interest is intellectual and when he takes sides (and he does take them!) he can be trusted more than anyone else because in his decision the "I" is not involved. The great intensity of Einstein's thought is directed outside toward the world of phenomena. No one expressed more clearly this aloofness toward the world of human affairs than Einstein himself in *The World As I See It*:

> My passionate interest in social justice and social responsibility has always stood in curious contrast to a marked lack of desire for direct association with men and women. I am

> a horse for single harness, not cut out for tandem or team work. I have never belonged wholeheartedly to country or state, to my circle of friends, or even to my own family. These ties have always been accompanied by a vague aloofness, and the wish to withdraw into myself increases with the years.
>
> Such isolation is sometimes bitter, but I do not regret being cut off from the understanding and sympathy of other men. I lose something by it, to be sure, but I am compensated for it in being rendered independent of the customs, opinions, and prejudices of others, and am not tempted to rest my peace of mind upon such shifting foundations.

Therefore, the external scenery of Einstein's life is of little importance.

He must have been shy and withdrawn as a child. The capability to wonder must have appeared early. In Einstein's memory, the greatest impression left from his childhood is the observation of a magnetic needle. It is this fact that he so often recalls when he speaks of his early years. He was not exceptionally brilliant as a student, neither at high school nor at the university. If I did not know this from Einstein I could easily have deduced it for myself. The most characteristic feature of his work is originality and obstinacy, the capability of travelling a lonely path for years and years, not the capability of learning, but of thinking and understanding. Schools and universities all over the world reward men who can easily tread a well-beaten path. The one who knows has an advantage over the one who wonders.

As a child and as a youth he wished to be left alone. The ideal life was, for him, that of least interference from the outside world. He was comparatively happy in Switzerland because there men are left to themselves and privacy is respected. The results of the thoughts he started when he was sixteen were published in 1905. This is the year in which his four celebrated papers appeared. His fame among physicists began some four years later. Einstein told me, "Before I was thirty, I never met a real physicist." In Einstein's case it was luck that he did not.

There was no one to discourage him, though I doubt whether anyone would have been successful, anyway.

The rest is the story of increasing success and rising fame. To give a few dates: he graduated from the Zürich Polytechnical School in Switzerland in 1901, then he worked in the Swiss Patent Office. Four years after special relativity theory was formulated he became an associate professor at the University of Zürich; then, in quick succession, a full professor in Prague and again a professor in Zürich. In 1913 he became a member of the Prussian Academy of Science and moved to Berlin. There he remained for the next seventeen years. Since 1933 he has lived in Princeton, New Jersey. He was married twice, once divorced and once widowed.

Of course, the rising fame was annoying to Einstein. It took much of his time, but it was not too important because nothing was ever important to him besides the understanding of the phenomena of nature.

In 1921, when I went to study in Berlin, I saw with amazement the disgraceful spectacle which attended Einstein's fame. It was still twelve years before Hitler. I saw conservative daily papers with editorials attacking Einstein's theory: "If he believes in his theory, let him answer our arguments. We shall be fair and we shall print his reply." I saw placards announcing lectures against Einstein's theory in one of Berlin's greatest concert halls. I was curious enough to buy a ticket and witness the performance. It was a double feature with two professors scheduled to speak. A man with a small beard and a monotonous voice read a manuscript to an overflowing audience, telling them how silly was special relativity theory with its paradox of the twins, that it was the greatest hoax in the history of science, that the attention paid to this subject was foreign to the truly German spirit. At that time, it still was not the right thing to attack Einstein openly as being Jewish, yet this was done not once, but hundreds of times in a more veiled form. On the surface there was the Weimar Republic in Germany, but beneath this thin wretched surface one could detect the seeds of coming turmoil.

I remember, too, that during the interval between two consecutive lectures, everyone was looking at the box in which Einstein sat. I don't know why he came, but he seemed to have a wonderful time greeting people and smiling broadly with a loud giggle and stealing the show just by his presence.

An amazing spectacle developed. All over the world popular lectures on relativity theory were delivered. There was even money in it. An American magazine—I don't remember the name—announced a prize of a few thousand dollars for an article on relativity theory that would explain it in three thousand words. For students in a country with inflation, such a great sum was almost beyond the imagination. I helped my friend with his entry and in my wretched room we put the finishing touches on an essay. As we counted the words, we dreamed about the rain of gold that relativity theory and the U.S.A. would bestow upon us. No, we did not win.

When later I went back to Poland, to my surprise I found the same atmosphere. The fame of relativity theory crossed all national frontiers. It was as vastly and passionately debated then as Communism is today. My professor in mathematics, Zaremba—and a very distinguished mathematician he was—gave a graduate lecture and many popular lectures against relativity theory. He argued that relativity theory is inconsistent with the definition of a rigid body. A rigid body is a body that does not contract. How, therefore, can a rigid stick contract when in motion? Of course, it was a trivial argument although my professor put it in heavy and learned language. The simple point, that the same bodies that we regard as rigid behave differently according to classical physics and special relativity theory, was not understood by the old professor nor would I have dared explain it to him. He was attacked in a very brutal way by another professor, also a distinguished mathematician and astronomer (his name was Banachiewicz), who called Zaremba blind and his arguments foolish. What happened in Cracow, my small university town, is interesting only because similar things happened all over the world. Popular lectures about relativity theory drew great crowds and bewildered audiences listened to the arguments pro and con. Even Einstein was persuaded to give public lectures on relativity theory. He was not a very good popularizer of his own doctrine, yet the public was charmed to see Einstein and to listen to his fine voice. During one of his lectures he played with a stick that lay on the table. One lady asked another, "Why doesn't he leave the stick alone?" But she soon saw the point. When Einstein showed by gestures how a stick moves and contracts, the relieved lady whispered to her neighbor, "I did not know that this is the contracting stick."

I, myself, was ready and willing to take part in these discussions and suffered when I was not asked to do so. A year later, in 1922, I was a high school teacher in a small Polish town. The excitement of relativity theory reached even there and I had the rare distinction of being the only man in this town who knew anything about relativity theory. I gave a series of four lectures and many had to be sent away because the room could not accommodate the crowd. Afterward one of my friends wisecracked, "I would much prefer to listen to Einstein lecturing about Infeld."

Slowly the arguments against relativity theory subsided. Nowadays no physicist doubts that the axioms of special and general relativity theory are superior to those of classical physics. He may doubt whether the revolution is radical enough, but no one in his proper senses believes that a retreat into the position of classical physics is possible. Even later, when Hitler came to power, papers on relativity theory were still printed in Germany. This was considered all right as long as the name of the creator of relativity theory was omitted.

Even if one understands why Einstein's fame started suddenly one does not understand so easily why it still prevails. There are different reasons. I believe one is that some of the Herren Professoren fought him just a little too bitterly for their own good. The other reason is that Einstein is colorful. You sense it when you glance at any of his pictures. If Einstein were to enter your room at a party and be introduced to you as Mr. Eisenstein of whom you knew nothing, you would still be fascinated by the brilliance of his eyes, by his shyness and gentleness, by his delightful sense of humor, by the fact that he can twist platitudes into wisdom, and that whatever he might say would be the product of his own mind uninfluenced by the shrieks of the outside world. You feel that before you is a man who thinks for himself. He has influenced millions, but in a deeper sense he can be influenced by no one.

During the First World War and later, one saw Einstein entering the arena of politics, or rather being pushed into it. He takes sides. He has contempt for violence, for bullying, for aggression, for injustice. "Contempt" is, I believe, the right word. It would be wrong to use the word "hatred," instead. He is always kind and because of the strong impact of the external world he learns to go through the motions of being interested and of concealing his inner detachment. His appearance helps. His striking face of a great artist or prophet, his eyes that seem to radiate, may deceive you if you talk to Einstein. Their radiation is directed far into the world and the laws that govern it and not toward your personal problems. Yet he will gladly, with a witty remark and loud laugh, sign a letter of recommendation as long as he has not a definite proof that you are a crook or incompetent. He believes what you tell him because he is kind, because he wishes to be kind and because it is much simpler to believe than to disbelieve. You may think that one can convince Einstein of anything, but he will become stubborn and unbending if he finds out that you are a Fascist. He will become suspicious if you come with a project that seems to benefit him and not you.

In 1914, he refused to sign the Manifesto of the German scientists. After the First World War he was the first German scientist to be invited to France.

His most important participation in the affairs of our world came in 1939. The story of how physicists tried unsuccessfully to interest the Army and Navy in the Atomic Project is told in the Smyth report with subtle understatements and omissions. It was the famous letter of Einstein to Roosevelt that broke the rigidity of the military mind. Einstein, who has contempt for violence and for wars, is regarded as the father of the Atomic Bomb. This is so because the modern history of the development of atomic energy starts with Einstein's equivalence relation between mass and energy. This is also so because the history of the Atomic Bomb starts with Einstein's letter.

In these dark times when the air is filled with empty platitudes, silly arguments, tales of little men, it is refreshing to listen to the clear voice that speaks for reason. It is the aloof conscience of the world that tells us (*Only Then Shall We Be Free*):

> Science has brought forth this danger, but the real problem is in the minds and hearts of men. We will not change the hearts of other men by mechanisms, but by changing *our* hearts and speaking bravely.
>
> We must be generous in giving to the world the knowledge we have of the forces of nature, after establishing safeguards against abuse.
>
> We must be not merely willing but actively eager to submit ourselves to binding authority necessary for world security.
>
> We must realize we cannot simultaneously plan for war and peace.
>
> When we are clear in heart and mind—only then shall we find courage to surmount the fear which haunts the world.

In seeking to understand Einstein's appeal to the imagination of so many of his fellow men, a strange comparison comes to my mind. In a village in India there is a wise old saint. He sits under a tree and never speaks. The people look at his eyes directed toward heaven. They do not know the thoughts of this old man because he is always silent. But they form their own image of the saint, a picture that comforts them. They sense deep wisdom and kindness in his eyes. They bring food to the tree where the man sits, happy that by this small sacrifice they form a communion with the lofty thoughts of their saint.

In our civilization we do not have primitive villagers and silent, contemplating saints. Yet we see in our newspapers a picture of a man who does not go to the barber, who does not wear a tie or socks, whose eyes seem to be directed away from the little things of our world. He does not toil for personal comfort. He cares little for all the things that mean so much in our lives. If he speaks in defense of a cause he does not do it for his personal glory. It is comforting for us to know that such a man still exists, a man whose thoughts are directed toward the stars. We give him admiration because in admiring him we prove to ourselves that we, too, yearn for the distant stars.

Einstein has become a symbol for many, a monument people have built, a symbol that they need for their own comfort.

And perhaps, in the last analysis, these people are right. Perhaps the real greatness of Einstein lies in the simple fact that, though in his life he has gazed at the stars, yet he also tried to look at his fellow men with kindness and compassion.

EVENTS IN THE LIFE OF EINSTEIN

1879 —Born at Ulm, Bavaria (Germany).

1880–1894—Spent in Munich where he attended the Gymnasium.

1894 —Family moved to Milan, Italy.

1896–1901—Studied in Switzerland at the Zürich Polytechnical School.

1901 —Became a Swiss citizen; worked in Patent Office in Bern; first marriage.

1905 —The appearance of papers on Quantum Theory, Relativity Theory, Brownian Motion. Became lecturer (*Privat-dozent*) at Bern University.

1909 —Associate (*Ausserordentlicher*) professor at the University of Zürich.

1910 —Professor of theoretical physics at the German University in Prague.

1912 —Professor of theoretical physics at the Zürich Polytechnical School.

1913 —Member of the Prussian Academy; moved to Berlin.

1916 —Work on General Relativity essentially finished; second marriage.

1919 —Confirmation of General Relativity theory, by observation of the deflection of light in a gravitational field.

1919–1932—Visited U.S.A., England, France, China, Japan, Palestine, Spain. In 1922, received the Nobel prize for his theory of the photoelectric effect.

1933 —Resigned from the Prussian Academy; became a professor at the Institute for Advanced Study, Princeton, New Jersey.

1945 —Official retirement.

BIBLIOGRAPHY

There is a tremendous literature dealing with Relativity Theory, on all possible levels. I shall mention only the books that were written at least partially by Einstein. This seems to me to be the only reasonable method of selection here, in order to avoid pages of bibliography.

Non-Technical Books

A. Einstein: Relativity; the special and general theory, 138 pp., New York (Holt) 1920.

This is Einstein's popular book on relativity, mentioned in Chapter I.

A. Einstein: Sidelights on relativity, 56 pp., London (Methuen), 1922.

Contains lectures "Ether and relativity" and "Geometry and experience."

A. Einstein: The world as I see it, 290 pp., New York (Covici Friede), 1934.

A collection of letters, articles, speeches on different subjects.

A. Einstein and L. Infeld: The evolution of physics, 313 pp., New York (Simon and Schuster), 1938.

Books on a More Technical Level

A. Einstein: The meaning of relativity, 135 pp. (Princeton University Press), 1945.

A second edition of Einstein's lectures on relativity theory delivered in 1921.

A. Einstein: The principle of relativity, 186 pp., Calcutta (University of Calcutta), 1920.

Contains reprints of Einstein's original papers and those of Minkowski.

ACKNOWLEDGMENTS

While writing this book, I made a point of not consulting any sources besides Einstein's writings. I am therefore grateful to my graduate student, George Duff, for his critical reading of the manuscript and checking it for mistakes or omissions; to Helen, to Beulah Harris, and Professor Coxeter, who read the manuscript and made very helpful comments. My special thanks are due to Mr. Charles Scribner, Jr., who edited this book with care, sympathy and understanding.

SELECTIVE INDEX